LIFEGUIDE

Debbie Pollitt

Boxtree

First published in the UK 1990 by Boxtree Limited
36 Tavistock Street
London WC2E 7PB

Published in association with Granada Television/This Morning

Text © Debbie Pollitt 1991
Chapter Three 'Feeling Fit' © Dr John Williams

Designed by ML Design
Cover design by Edward Pitcher
Cover illustration by Anthony Sidwell
Line drawings by Sharon Worthington

Height/weight chart and breast examination photographs ©
the Health Education Authority, reproduced with kind
permission

The publishers and author would like to thank
Granada Television for the use of other photographs

Printed and bound by the Bath Press, Avon

A CIP catalogue entry for this book is available from the
British Library

ISBN 1-85283-145-6

CONTENTS

FOREWORD

BY DENISE ROBERTSON
THIS MORNING AGONY AUNT AND CREATOR OF *LIFEGUIDE*

'If only...'. These words crop up in so many of the letters I receive at *This Morning*. 'If only I had more confidence...'; 'If only I had a partner or a friend...', and the most frequent of all: 'If only I could lose some weight...'.

Quite often viewers will see one of the *This Morning* 'makeovers' as the answer to their problem. They are sure that a new hairstyle, wardrobe and make-up technique will transform their lives. Even if it were possible to offer 'makeovers' to everyone I am doubtful about instant solutions to deep-seated problems.

Through *Lifeguide* we hope to offer not only transformation but a deeper inspection of what makes us unhappy or prevents us from achieving our full potential. Our belief in the power of mutual support has been strengthened by the springing up of *Lifeguide* groups in various parts of the country and we have been delighted by the response, we have received from so many people.

We have looked at diet, health, fitness and bad habits like smoking because happiness is difficult to achieve if you feel under par or know you don't look your best. Work figures in *Lifeguide* as well as preparation for retirement. Nowadays we can expect longer, fuller lives and it is vital that those bonus years should be full of warmth and laughter, excitement and satisfaction. 'If only...' is a sad phrase at twenty and is even more poignant at seventy-five.

We have also tried to show how learning the power of positive thinking can help you to achieve your goals and along with new ways of thinking we have included sources of help, whether you are planning a change of lifestyle on seeking solutions to problems. We have compiled a comprehensive list for easy reference at the end of each chapter.

Most people want good relationships, with lovers, family or friends, and it is difficult to be loved and liked if you do not love and value yourself. Too often our childhood training teaches us to undervalue ourselves, to believe that we do not measure up to some unknown and unattainable standard. If we carry this lack of self-worth into adult life we are heading for difficulties. A broken relationship or the loss of a job can shatter our already fragile self-esteem.

Lifeguide aims to help you assess yourself correctly, to acknowledge your good points while admitting to and rectifying your faults. We want *Lifeguide* members to be proud of what they are and prouder still of what they can become, regardless of age, size, status, education or physical condition. That is why you won't see 'perfect' men and women on *Lifeguide*. We have the best of instructors and experts but the people doing the exercises and discussing the problems are ordinary mortals who want to turn 'If only' into, 'Didn't we do it well.'

INTRODUCTION

BY SIUBHAN RICHMOND,
PRODUCER AND PRESENTER OF *LIFEGUIDE*

'You can't always control what happens to you, but you can control the way you react to it,' Colin Rose said to me as we packed up the camera after our first interview for *Lifeguide*. TV experts have a nasty habit of coming out with these golden nuggets of wisdom just after you've finished shooting. The cameraman looked at me, pausing in his packing - he sensed that the working day was not quite over after all! Psychologist and author of *The Mind and Body Diet*, Colin Rose, had, as far I was concerned, hit the nail on the head. Over the next few months, as we rushed around Britain, talking to *Lifeguide* members about their lives, discussing advice with experts, digging out tracksuits, diet sheets and self-help books, a few more nails were firmly hammered into place.

Everybody's story is different - circumstances vary, each personality is unique, but as human beings we all share common characteristics of biology and psychology. It became obvious to me that there were a few general lessons we could learn from *Lifeguide* that could be crucial in our plan to change or improve our lives.

First of all, we needed to know what people wanted from life, and therefore from *Lifeguide*. Denise Robertson sat in the studio with Richard and Judy and asked the nation if people could possibly write in and let us know. Could they? The letters flooded in and as we read through them all I was struck by their similarity.

The general goal was 'happiness' - but this was usually seen as conditional upon losing weight, gaining confidence, enjoying life more.

It was a rather daunting challenge; the most we could hope to do on the programme was point people in the right direction, to offer some practical advice on looking and feeling good.

We constantly stressed that ultimately it was up to the individual to help him—or herself. We could only suggest ideas and hope to inspire people to stop and think carefully about themselves and their lives. And that brings me to the first of those lessons we learnt on *Lifeguide*: self-knowledge is crucial to self-improvement.

You need to be honest - to yourself and about yourself. What is it that you want to change? Why do you want to change it? What is holding you back? The more you understand about your behaviour, the better chance you have of changing it. Do you get depressed when someone shouts at you and tells you that you are stupid? Do you then take comfort in a piece of chocolate cake? If so, stop and think about your reaction; for a start, reaching for food in times of stress is simply a bad habit. And so to lesson number two: habits rule your life and can make or break your chance of succeeding with your personal goals.

INTRODUCTION

One of our key phrases is: 'You can't always control what happens to you , but you can control the way you react to it.' If eating for comfort is a habit, your diet will fail every time you get upset. If smoking is a habit, you could die. Good habits can be learnt and bad habits can be broken.

Exercise positive thinking and remember that your mind and your body are not two separate entities. 'You can't always control what happens to you, but you can control the way you react to it.' The way you think affects the way you behave. When someone calls you stupid, do you automatically think, 'Yes, I am, I'm a failure; oh, I'm so depressed (where's that chocolate cake?)'? That is negative thinking and that can become a habit of mind (as well as making you fat).

Another lesson well learnt: respect time. You need time to yourself, thinking space to help you learn about yourself. The wisest men are usually hermits, spending most of their life alone in thought and meditation. You may find that a bit extreme, not to mention a trifle lonely... Seriously though, set aside some time, however short, to relax and to think positively. You need time to break bad habits and develop good ones. So don't give up too early - whether you're trying to lose weight, get fit, learn a new skill, write a book or stop smoking, stick with it! Neither Rome, nor *Lifeguide*, was made in a day.

Most importantly, you need time to enjoy yourself, to enjoy life. Regularly spend time doing something that makes you happy; after all, if that's one of your goals in life, you'll need to practise it as often as possible.

Lifeguide is a holistic approach to a healthy and happy life, acknowledging that your behaviour does not occur in isolation to your thoughts and emotions. Your personal success depends on many different factors and we cannot supply a ready-made formula. This book is neither a complete self-help manual or a definitive guide to Life (that will certainly take wiser men and women than ourselves); we hope simply to help you stop and think about yourself and your life, to provide a guide to practical matters: where to go for advice, information and help; an insight into other people's lives to highlight our common fears, goals and successes.

As we've learnt from *Lifeguide*, success comes that much more easily with a little help from your friends and with any luck it'll also come easier with a little help from *Lifeguide*.

LIFEGUIDE GROUPS

When we started making the television series of *Lifeguide* in August 1990 we decided that we needed some input from the public. What did they think, for instance, about the subjects we were planning to cover? We invited some of the people who had written to *Lifeguide* to tell us more about themselves and to enable us to see whether we were in fact on the right track.

Getting together with the viewers like this was a wonderful experience and we realised that if we were going to be at all successful, then we had to really listen to their needs. When you're dealing with sensitive issues on television such as depression, stress and low self-esteem it is vital that you don't lose sight of who your audience really is. Once we had met the women who later became *Lifeguide* members, we felt inspired to produce the sort of programmes that they wanted to see. So, for instance, although many of them said that their problem was weight, they didn't just want another diet programme. They wanted to know why they were overweight in the first place, and why they felt depressed so much of the time. Above all, they wanted to know how they could change their lives and how they could learn to be happier and more fulfilled.

They wanted to find out how they could deal with the cause of their problem, instead of just with the consequences. After all, what is the point of losing weight to stop feeling depressed when being depressed in the first place is what has made you put the weight on? Losing the weight is often dealing mainly with the consequence of the depression, not necessarily the cause. And without the remarkable honesty of these women, *Lifeguide* would not have been as successful as it has been.

We began with seven members in the original *Lifeguide* group. They bravely came along to the studios in Liverpool for a group discussion which we filmed. All of the people who joined the group said that just talking about their problems and discovering that they were not alone, that others had similar problems, had helped them enormously. Obviously we couldn't invite all our viewers to the discussion - so the next best thing was to let them see the group in action on the programme. We were a little worried that by installing a film crew and cameras, the women would feel inhibited and that we might lose some of the initial spontaneity and warmth. But although everyone was understandably nervous at first, within five minutes they had practically forgotten the crew was there.

A lack of confidence so strong that it was preventing them from fulfilling their ambitions and achieving their goals linked all these women. Yet they went through with what was probably quite a gruelling experience in the *Lifeguide* group - not only the pressure of a film crew watching their every expression and catching their every word, but also making the decision to commit themselves to *Lifeguide* over a long period of time.

We have stressed the importance of groups throughout the series because we have had unremitting evidence of the benefits of this form of self help. Experiencing problems of any kind can make you feel isolated and helpless. it helps to know that many other people are feeling just like you do and the moral support and friendship that you can offer to each other can provide just the boost you need in your desire for a more fulfilling and enjoyable lifestyle. Joining a group, or even setting up your own,is a positive step in itself so why not find out what's avaiLable in your area. If there is nothing which seems to fit your needs, why not start your own group? invite a friend and ask them to bring a friend too (a group doesn't have to mean a huge number: three people constitute as much of a group as thirty!) or put postcards in newsagents and post office windows for likeminded people to join you. Once you've read our *Lifeguide* members' stories, you will see for yourself what you can achieve by getting together with others.

LIFEGUIDE GROUPS

CAROL: *LIFEGUIDE* MEMBER

Carol is 26. She is a housewife and has two small children. Like others in the group, Carol had a weight problem and a real lack of self-confidence. She had also been suffering from post-natal depression after the birth of her second baby.

Since joining Lifeguide, Carol has learnt to spend time on herself - difficult when you're the busy mother of two small children. She had reached a point before joining Lifeguide when life seemed to hold no hope. She was tired, depressed and overweight. But she made the positive decision to find a way to feel better. Her goals included getting fit, losing weight and starting a career. She felt encouraged to organise her goals, to write them down and commit herself to achieving them.

She started with going swimming twice a week which gave her not only a physical boost, but a psychological one too; exercise does make you feel better. She allowed herself to feel proud of her achievements. and going swimming gave her the opportunity of doing something by herself, for herself. Even though it was only one hour twice a week, she felt that she could get away without having to worry about the family.

Discussing her problems with others in the group gave Carol the confidence and strength to make some decisions about her life. She says, 'In the past whenever I have brought up the subject of doing things outside the home with my husband, he's always laughed at me. but since I've joined Lifeguide he's realised that I'm serious about it. We've discussed things together and I've made the decision to start night school. This way I'll learn new skills so that I can look for a job.I feel great about the future now and I'm positive about my ability to get fit and lose weight.'

CHAPTER ONE

POSITIVE THINKING

CHAPTER ONE

POSITIVE THINKING

FOR A BETTER QUALITY OF LIFE

Positive thinking is a philosophy which can change your life for the better. It is an attitude which can help you to help yourself to deal with problems large and small by enabling you to take control of your life.

So, before we go any further, let's see how you feel about your life - answer **YES** or **NO** where appropriate:

1. **Do you like yourself?**
2. **Are you proud of your achievements?**
3. **Are you happy with the way you look?**
4. **Do you make most of the decisions about your life?**
5. **Do you feel in control of your life?**
6. **Do you feel valued?**
7. **Do you set time aside for yourself?**
8. **Do you enjoy your life?**

If you answered **YES** to some or all of these questions then congratulations! You already have more positives in your life than negatives - you make decisions about how you want your life to be. You don't allow situations to continue which are making you unhappy. You know that you are important and that you need time for yourself. Because you feel good about yourself, you look good too. Because you like yourself, others do too.

If you answered **NO** to any of these questions, *don't despair*! You can learn to take control of your life. You can learn to like yourself and achieve a more fulfilling lifestyle.

POSITIVE THINKING

Through positive thinking you can start to make things happen *for* you instead of waiting for things to happen to you. Above all, you can learn to be happy.

WHAT IS POSITIVE THINKING?

Lifeguide expert on positive thinking, author and psychologist Vera Peiffer, defines it as:

'*...making use of the suggestibility of your subconscious mind in a positive way.*'

So the negative assumptions which are rooted in your subconscious and which prevent you from achieving your goals can be turned into positive assumptions which can help you to achieve those goals. So how does it work? Here's an experiment which you can try out now which will illustrate the power of your imagination.

THE PENDULUM EXPERIMENT

1. Take a piece of string and either a ring, a key or a pen with a clip. Tie the object to one end of the string.

2. Fasten the other end of the string to your right index finger.

3. Sit at a table and rest both your elbows on the table, whilst supporting your right wrist with your left hand.

4. Bring your right index finger down far enough so that the object on the end of the string rests gently on the table.

5. Gently lift your index finger upwards so that the object comes up off the table and hangs still.

NOTE: *It is vital that you do not move your right hand*

6. Now make the object the focus of your attention. Stare at it and *imagine* that it begins to swing from left to right. Visualise the movement, see it in your mind moving from left to right, from left to right, from left to right.   Say that to yourself: 'left to right to left to right.'

7. You will now see that the object has actually begun to swing from left to right, just as you have imagined it.

8. Continue imagining the object swinging. The object will swing very slightly at first. Imagine how the swinging movement left to right becomes more pronounced. Now see how the object is actually swinging harder, left to right.

9. Lower your hand and once again rest the object on the table.

10. Lift the object again so that it hangs still and free - remember to keep your hand perfectly still - but this time imagine that it is swinging in a clockwise circle. Move your eyes around the object in a clockwise circle. Continue to imagine the clockwise circle and you will see that the object does begin to swing in a clockwise circle.

Have you done it? Congratulations! If you can make the object swing in the direction you have imagined, you are capable of using the 'suggestibility of your subconscious mind' to make other things happen in your life!

Think about what has happened during Vera's experiment. You have constructed a situation in which your will-power conflicts with your imagination. You were determined not to move your hand during the experiment. Your hand represents your will-power or determination. But your imagination (represented by the movement of the object) made the object move in spite of your hand being still.

NOTE: *When your will-power conflicts with your imagination, your imagination will always win out*

 So how can this affect your everyday life? Well, take the example of a driving test. You want to pass the test (your will-power) but you imagine (the suggestibility of your subconscious mind) that you will fail. What happens? You may very well fail your test!

WHAT ARE THE CONSCIOUS AND SUBCONSCIOUS MINDS?

Like anything else, if you are to learn how to be a positive thinker, you need to know a little about the theory before you can succeed at the practice. Think, then, of the mind as a two-part system. There is the **conscious** mind and the **subconscious** mind. The conscious mind deals with our everyday decision-making and helps to deal with new situations in which we need to apply a bit of logical and rational sense. For instance, when you first learn to drive a car, your decisions are made **consciously**. When you are pulling away from a stationary position in the first few months or so of driving, you will **consciously** think, 'I must use the first gear to set off, then I must change to second,' and so on. That is **conscious** thought and decision.

POSITIVE THINKING

The **subconscious** part of our mind is the bit that's hidden. Vera Peiffer explains that 'the subconscious mind deals with the repetitions of learned behaviour'. So, for an experienced driver, changing gears becomes a **subconscious** thought process. That is, you are not **consciously** aware of making the decision to change from first gear to second gear. You do it automatically or **subconsciously**. You are probably **consciously** thinking about what to wear tonight or what to cook for dinner. Your **subconscious** mind is dealing with the problem of changing gear. So can you see the pattern? At the beginning, an inexperienced driver has to **consciously** decide which gears to use. Once the driver has made the correct decision, and repeated the action several times, the information is fed into the **subconscious** mind. There it is stored until needed the next time, leaving your **conscious** mind clear for other things.

Vera Peiffer explains that there is a 'Facts-Memory-Behaviour' chain which works like this:

FACTS = conscious experience

MEMORY = memory of feelings accompanying the experience

BEHAVIOUR = the way we behave in the same situation again

EXAMPLE: A child falls into a river and nearly drowns. The child experiences fear, shock and anxiety.

POSITIVE THINKING

FACT: The incident itself and the accompanying feelings are stored away in the subconscious.

MEMORY: The next time that child goes near water, he will experience the same feelings of fear and anxiety. He will avoid the water because he is frightened.

BEHAVIOUR: So when we find that we cannot cope with a situation, this will feed our subconscious mind with negative information and with a memory and sense of failure. When the person is again in a similar position, the assumption that he cannot cope will be automatic. That is the person will *expect* to feel bad because he *imagines* he will feel bad. Because our imagination will always win over our will-power, the person is bound within the negative confines of his imagination.

Any feelings which are fed into and stored in the memory will always emerge in the form of behaviour.

Consider this scenario:

Anne is married to John. John has an active and successful career. Anne works at home, looking after their two children and running the house. John has an unfortunate tendency to underestimate Anne's role in their lives. He belittles her, reminding her how hard he works, how lucky she is to have a husband like him. After 20 years of marriage to John, Anne now believes that what he says is true. She believes she *is* lucky, and that she *is* worthless compared to him. When first married, she had a sense of her own worth and she had pride in herself and her work. But John's repeated verbal abuse of her (and it is abuse) that she is useless and worthless has been inferred by Anne and stored in her subconscious mind, together with the memory of the feelings she experiences each time he says these things (a sense of failure, depression, anxiety). She imagines that she is useless, worthless and incapable of achieving anything. Because she imagines this, it becomes in effect true. She does not tackle new situations because the subconscious message to herself is that she is incapable of being successful. John's accusations have now become true, even if they weren't in the beginning.

You can see the pattern. Anne infers the repeated negative message from John. It is fed directly into her subconscious mind. When she tries to do anything new, because of the negative information stored in her subconscious mind, she assumes she is incapable of succeeding. So she does not try.

Anne could take steps to improve her sense of self-worth and self-esteem. She could decide to take control of her feelings and therefore her life by turning her negative assumptions into positive assumptions. She is a failure only because she *imagines* she is a failure.

Now do this exercise to help you eliminate your negative assumptions about yourself:

1. **Find a private place (probably the bathroom) where you can stand and look in a mirror.**

2. **Repeat a positive message to yourself which is appropriate to your particular problem. For instance:**

*   **'I am a likeable person'** *OR*

*   **'I like myself because I'm kind/funny/clever'**

3. **Repeat the message 10 or 15 times.**

POSITIVE THINKING

Don't be put off by the simplicity of this exercise - it
works if you do it frequently enough: at least three times
every day - when you first wake in the morning, during
the day and at night before you go to sleep. If you can't
get to a private enough place, repeat the message silently
to yourself. If repeated negative facts can affect the way
you feel about yourself and the way you behave, it follows
that positive facts can too. You can influence, then, your
'Facts-Memory-Behaviour' chain so that it works
positively for you.

But do remember that 'information has to be given
repeatedly before it takes root in the subconscious mind
and that an incident has to be accompanied by a
particularly strong emotion to impress itself on the
subconscious and thus influence consequent behaviour'
(Peiffer). So don't imagine that because one person says
one horrible thing to you that it is going to become
rooted in your subconscious and affect all your future
behaviour, because it won't.

*So, if we want to influence our behaviour or our performance,
we have to do so via our subconscious mind; we have to select
new and positive thoughts which we repeatedly feed into our
conscious mind because repeated thoughts take root in the
subconscious mind.*

Positive thinking, then, can help you to realise your
ambitions because it enables you to have faith in yourself.
You really are what you imagine yourself to be. If you
think you are a failure, you will be a failure. If you think
you are competent, you will be competent. We put things
off for a variety of reasons -perhaps you recognise some
of them... 'I just haven't got the time!'; 'I'm not clever

enough'; 'I'm not very good at that sort of thing'. We believe that by adopting a strategy of positive thinking, most things are possible. Take the writing of this book, for instance. I had moments before I started when I panicked at the responsibility of starting such a project. I thought that I could never do such an enormous thing. But then I sat down at my desk, worked it all out, planned the chapter headings and realised that in fact I *could* do it. But it was me who reversed those brief moments of panic. Rather than waste time worrying about not being able to write the book, I concentrated on how I *could* do it.

KEY WORDS:
'Positive' and 'Choice'

So, as Vera Peiffer says, 'Being positive means worrying less and enjoying more, choosing to look at the good side rather than filling your mind with gloom and doom, choosing to be happy rather than unhappy.'

TAKING RESPONSIBILITY FOR YOUR FEELINGS

Accepting responsibility for the way you feel is a crucial part of learning to be a positive thinker. It is a fact that things will happen in your life over which you have little or no control. You cannot control other people's behaviour or actions. But what you *can* control is your perception of and reaction to events and behaviour. You have the choice to adopt a positive frame of mind and therefore be better able to cope well in certain situations. You are not responsible for how other people behave but you are responsible for yourself. Taking responsibility for your feelings and your reactions to events means that you may have to face some uncomfortable facts about yourself. Do you blame your

POSITIVE THINKING

bad tempers and moods on external events or other people's behaviour? If so, you are not taking responsibility for your feelings. If you have had a problematic day at work and you end the day feeling stressed and irritable, think about what caused these feelings. It was not the events themselves, but *your reaction to them.* Thinking negatively means that you have been unable to cope efficiently with the problems in hand.

NOTE: *'It is of fundamental importance that you look after yourself and work on achieving happiness for yourself'*

• *Be open, friendly and helpful - but don't be a doormat*

• *Decide what you want and go for it - but don't be a bully*

• *Be optimistic - but be realistic*

• *Have faith in yourself - but take an interest in other people*

This should be your first priority. Only when you are feeling good about yourself can you achieve a level of happiness. And if you are positive about yourself, others will be positive towards you. If you think your whole world is about to collapse because something has gone wrong at work, then your whole world *will* seem to collapse - you will be feeling angry and resentful and you may have rows with other people because of these feelings. Other things may go wrong because your attention is taken up with feeling bad about the original problem. Negative thinking, then, can set you on a downward spiral unless you decide to take charge of your feelings and be positive.

The difference between a positive thinker and a negative thinker is that when faced with a problem, the positive thinker sees that problem as a challenge. Having faith in yourself alters the perspective on many problems. It gives you the facility to accept some blame, to cope with criticism without falling to pieces, to overcome fear, to be successful in achieving your goals.

Similarly, Vera Peiffer believes that, 'In the long run, taking responsibility for your actions is a winning strategy because it opens doors to a completely new range of possibilities for becoming a successful person. When I speak of success I am speaking of a number of different areas, like health, wealth, happiness and personal fulfilment.'

ACTION STATIONS!

1. Decide that you are going to take responsibility for yourself, your feelings and your actions. You can't change the way the world works but you can change your reaction to it.

2. Make a list of your present situation so that you can see which areas in your life are causing you problems. For instance, health, marriage, partnership, family, finances, job, self-confidence, friends.

3. Make a separate list of the areas in which you want to make changes, putting the most pressing problems first. Only deal with one item on the list at a time.

4. Look at the first point you have decided to deal with. Let's say it's your job. Decide what it is about your job that is causing you problems. Identify aspects of the situation you can change (your own attitude and behaviour) and those you can't change (other people's attitude and behaviour, unforeseen events). So, you can't change your colleagues unpleasant behaviour, but you can change your reaction to it.

5. Now make another list, this time recording your goals. Remember to set goals which are realistically attainable, because if you set yourself impossible targets you won't genuinely be able to believe you can succeed. If you don't believe you can succeed, you

POSITIVE THINKING

EXAMPLE:

GOALS	TIME LIMIT Within.....
To Change my job	3 Months
To Lose 3 Stone (19.5kgs)	3 Months
To make new friends	2-6 Months
To pass my driving test	3-4 Months

won't. It sometimes helps to give yourself a time limit when setting your goals - but again, be realistic. After all, you're not going to lose three stone (19.5 kg) in a week, are you?

6. Do your research. If your goal is to lose some weight, think about how you can provide yourself with a nutritious and healthy eating plan which will fit into your lifestyle. Think about what your social plans are during the time you plan to lose weight - perhaps you've been invited to dinner somewhere. If so, work out how you will cope with this situation. Why not make the decision to eat what you like for just one night and not to feel guilty about what you eat. Feel positive about it and see it as a reward for all the hard work you're going to put in between now and then. Similarly, if your goal is to make new friends, investigate the best ways of doing this. What local events, for instance, would provide a social outlet? Is there an an activity which you would enjoy doing and where you would meet like-minded people? Can you comfortably fit it into your life?

7. Repeat your positive messages as directed. Resist the temptation to give up on your goals. Make a list of the benefits of achieving your goals. Passing your driving test, for instance, will mean that you have more freedom and flexibility. You won't have to sit and wait for buses or rely on lifts from other people.

8. Learn to relax. Use the relaxation exercise at the end of this chapter to help get into a positive frame of mind. If you can feel your resolutions slipping when a problem crops up, do the relaxation exercise immediately.

9. Visualise your achievements. If you are going to become slim, imagine yourself as a slim person in an everyday situation - at work, for instance, or at the swimming baths with the kids, on holiday or even around the house.

10. Be positive about achieving your goals. Use positive language to describe what you are doing: don't say, 'I would like to be...', say instead, 'I am going to be slim,' or 'I am going to pass my driving test.'

11. Learn not to punish yourself. If you have a minor set-back in the process of achieving your goals, don't give up and don't feel as though you have failed. See each set back as part of the learning process.

12. Recognise your achievements. Feel proud of the 2 lb (1.8 kg) you've lost, or of asserting yourself at work. Treat yourself to a present or an evening pampering yourself at home. You've done well through your own efforts! Congratulations!

Becoming a positive thinker means that you have to make some changes in your life. People are notoriously frightened of change and will go to extraordinary lengths to avoid it. Don't be one of those people. Fear of change is a negative impulse in itself. See the changes as positive challenges en route to achieving your goals. It won't be easy but the rewards are great. Why put off being happy when you can be happy now?

RELAXATION

This exercise can help to relieve the immediate physical and mental tension you are experiencing:
*   find a private, quiet place where you can sit or lie down.

POSITIVE THINKING

- keep your arms and legs unfolded - crossing them will only make you feel even more tense.
- place one hand on your stomach above your navel
- make sure your teeth are not clenched
- let your shoulders drop
- ensure your fists are unclenched
- let your legs become floppy and relaxed
- close your eyes and be aware of the position of your body, whether you are setting in a chair or lying on a bed or the floor: concentrate on the different parts of your body in turn - first your head, then your arms, then your torso, then your legs and then your feet.
- listen to your breathing and count 10 to 15 breaths
- now take deeper breaths. Breathe in through your belly. If you are doing this correctly, your hand will rise and fall with the movement.
- breathe in through your belly, feeling your hand rise. Hold the breath for 5 seconds. And breathe out again. Repeat this 10 times.
- let your breathing become normal again.
- gently tighten all you muscles and open your eyes as you release the tension.

You should feel calmer now.

PAMELA: *LIFEGUIDE* MEMBER

Pamela is 28. She is married with one young son. She is a part-time medical secretary at her local hospital. She originally joined Lifeguide because she needed help in becoming motivated and gaining confidence. Much of her lack of confidence was, she felt, because she was very overweight. Like the others in the group, Pamela felt inspired by the discussions and realised that through positive thinking, she could in fact achieve not only the weight loss but the confidence too.

Pamela used Colin Rose's Mind and Body Diet to help her to overcome her negative self-expectations. She has now lost three stone (19.5 kg) and feels terrific. Pamela says, 'I feel much more confident and I have more energy than I ever had before. Positive thinking and believing that you can achieve what you want to achieve does work... along with the support I've got through coming to the Lifeguide group.'

ANNE LUCAS: *LIFEGUIDE* MEMBER

Anne is in her late 30s. She is a housewife. She joined Lifeguide because she lacked confidence. She associated this lack of confidence with being overweight. Unlike many of the other Lifeguide members, she had already taken positive steps towards achieving her goals by joining a slimming club. This had helped her to lose four stone (25 kg) with four still to go when we met her. her lack of confidence had been improved greatly already, and she gave the group such positive messages about her experiences: she had discovered that setting goals and giving herself rewards were vital for achieving anything. She felt that her weight was important; she lacked confidence because she hated the way she looked. But more important is the decision to feel positive about yourself, she thought.

Anne has now lost nearly all her excess weight and feels wonderful. She says, 'I can't deny that the weight loss was important., but the key factor is learning to like yourself. Discussing my experiences with other people has helped me to feel more confident and I,ve learnt to feel proud of my achievements. I've learnt to like myself first and the rest has followed.'

CHAPTER TWO

THE PROBLEM OF WEIGHT

THE PROBLEM OF WEIGHT

Let's apply a bit of positive thinking straight away - the fact is unless you have some medical condition which prevents weight loss (extremely rare, however much you think your glands are to blame!), most people can lose weight successfully and can maintain that weight loss. That includes you too!

From the letters we receive at the *Lifeguide* office, it is clear that being overweight is a big problem for the majority of our viewers. The thriving international diet industry is also testimony to the fact that few people find the key to maintaining a healthy ideal weight. We all want to feel good about ourselves, and look good too, but in recent years the quest to achieve a slim body has become an obsession with many women - and those who don't achieve this goal can experience an overwhelming sense of failure. Women can become depressed or even ill as a result of the pressure on them to be slim and their self-esteem plummets to an all time low - so where does this pressure come from?

I. THE BEAUTIFUL IDEAL

Every society has its own definition of beauty - we've all seen the pictures in the Sunday supplements of images of beautiful women from other cultures. To our western eyes, these women often don't seem beautiful. Perhaps they shave their heads, or paint colourful patterns on their cheeks... but in their own society, they *are* beautiful. Similarly they might look with horror at our long curled hair, or our coloured eyelids and lips and wonder how we could possibly think our style is attractive! In some societies, women are even encouraged to mutilate themselves for the sake of beauty. For instance, numerous metal rings around a woman's neck to make the neck longer - because a longer neck is the beautiful ideal. Or strong binding around the feet to restrict growth because small feet are regarded as a mark of distinction.

In our society the beautiful ideal is, above all other things, slimness. This ideal is presented to us in films, on television, in newspapers and magazines and in advertisements. Skinny models and actresses stare at us from the screens and the pages of the magazines - and what is the result? Most of us feel dissatisfied with the way we look and some of us have even become obsessive in our quest to be the beautiful ideal. And the media and the beauty and diet industries thrive on our discontent. Extreme casualties of the pressure to conform to an often unrealistic ideal are the people who develop the so-called slimming diseases, such as anorexia nervosa and bulimia. Victims of these diseases often transfer their worries and anxieties from other areas in their lives and perceive success in terms of their lack of body weight. After all, in our society, success is often portrayed as synonymous with being slim. Anorexia nervosa sufferers can literally starve themselves to death in an attempt to conform to the beautiful ideal.

NOTE:
Multi-million pound industries thrive on your dissatisfaction with your appearance

Not all of us can be a size 10. Our frames are different - if you have a large frame and you are, say 5'10" (1.78 m), there's no way you will ever realistically fit into a size 10. Of course we all want to look attractive - we know, for instance, that when we feel good, we look good - but we should be aware of the forces at work around us which

KEY PHRASES:
Positive thinking:
feeling good means
looking good

FACT:
To be very
overweight is
not healthy

NOTE:

Diseases which are
linked with obesity:
- Respiratory
  disorders -
  asthma/bronchitis
  can be
  exacerbated
- Hernias
- Arthritis
- Diabetes mellitus
- Circulatory
  problems
- Heart disease
- Gall bladder
  disorders
- Varicose veins
- High blood
  pressure
- Certain cancers

So you can see that
there are good
reasons to maintain
a healthy weight.

try and control our perceptions of attractive. Get to know and like your body. This might sound like too much of a cliche, but we really are all beautiful in some way. Find out what your healthy weight should be. If you are healthy, you will feel good, and if you feel good you will look good. Then aim to achieve that healthy weight. The beautiful ideal is promoted by the media and supported by the diet and beauty industries. Don't punish yourself because you don't fit this ideal.

2. THE HEALTHY IDEAL

If you are carrying around a significant amount of excess fat, your organs cannot function as efficiently as they should, you will be tired and lethargic a lot of the time, and your overall quality of life will suffer.

3. WHICH DIET

If you eat a healthy, balanced diet which fulfils all your nutritional needs and no more, you won't be fat. If you don't eat excessively, you won't be fat. This is not to say that you have to wave goodbye to all the things you love to eat. There is room within a healthy balanced diet for treats. A bit of chocolate and a few chips here and there won't make you fat. Eating should be a pleasure - nobody is saying that in order to be healthy you should deny yourself that pleasure. But you can derive pleasure from food without overeating. And you can get pleasure from eating nutritionally valuable food too.

In current popular jargon, the word diet has lost its true meaning. The fact is that your diet is your daily intake of food, whether it is low-calorie substitutes or chocolate cake and chips. When you decide to lose some weight, do you say, 'I'm going on a diet'? If so, you are probably one of the many people who spend their lives losing weight and putting it back on again. You are perceiving your weight loss as a temporary situation. You are cutting down your intake of food for a certain number of days or weeks, but then you are returning to normal eating. And then you put the weight back on again. So you 'go on a diet' again. And you lose the weight again. And you put the weight back on again. And so it goes on - short term weight loss is not the answer.

The answer is to find a permanent new healthy eating plan which suits your tastes, your body and your lifestyle. Instead of 'going on a diet', you simply change the way you eat. This way you can achieve a healthy, balanced diet, lose weight if you need to, and maintain your new healthy weight for the rest of your life. In other words, you can be in control of the way your body functions and looks.

4. THE WHOLE PERSON

REMEMBER:

- *be realistic about your goals - you might never be a size 10 but you can still be attractive*

- *be healthy above all else*

- *don't 'go on a diet' - it won't work!*

- *choose a sensible, healthy eating plan to suit your lifestyle*

Above all, you must aim to see your eating habits not as separate from but rather as part of your whole existence. As such, your eating plan must complement your lifestyle rather than conflict with it. Eat to live - not the other way round.

Now consult our WEIGHT/HEIGHT TABLE shown over the page - these weights are based on someone with a medium frame. So if you happen to be particularly small, don't panic and think that you're vastly overweight. If you are at all in doubt as to the size of your frame, consult your doctor. He or she will be able to tell you which category you fall into.

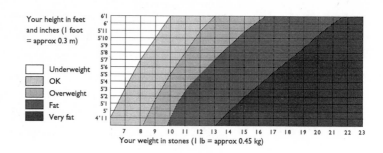

Now give yourself a quick refresher course in nutrition - you can only begin to eat healthily when you are armed with the right information.

NUTRITIONAL KNOW-HOW

Nutrients are the substances in food which are vital for life. Because the human body cannot manufacture most nutrients by itself, they must be obtained through food. If you want to get your body working efficiently by adopting a new eating plan for life, you need to know the benefits of eating certain kinds of foods. To achieve a healthy, balanced diet, you must have the right amounts of the different nutrients in your meals. So let's have a look at what the different nutrients actually are and what function they perform in maintaining your healthy body:

1. ESSENTIAL FATTY ACIDS (FATS)

NOTE:

Avoid saturated fats

Fat is necessary for insulating the body and as a source of energy. Too much fat, however, will very quickly be converted to unwanted extra body fat. Unsaturated, or polyunsaturated, fats are better for you than the saturated fats of meat, butter, and cream. Polyunsaturates are found mostly in corn oil, soya oil, sunflower oil and safflower oil and in polyunsaturated margarines. Most people eat far too much of the saturated fats which are associated with high cholesterol levels in arteries, often leading to heart trouble.

2. CARBOHYDRATES

These are the energy foods - the best kind are the complex carbohydrates contained in wholemeal bread, brown rice, wholemeal pasta and jacket potatoes. Although sugar is pure carbohydrate, it is a definite no-no in our healthy balanced diet. Too much can lead to all sorts of physical problems such as tooth decay, diabetes and heart disease. The body may not be able to cope with the excessive amounts of sugar contained in the modern refined diet and, although it is broken down into glucose to provide energy, the body may break it down too quickly and this can lead to problems in some people.

So eat the right kinds of carbohydrates - you need them to heat your body. But stay right away from refined white sugar. In this country each person takes in an astounding 100 lb (45.46kg) of sugar on average every year. Cutting down on sugar can be problematic - a surprising amount of prepared foods contain sugar, such as baked beans, soft drinks, biscuits etc. Start reading the nutritional value lists on the packets and tins - most foods have them nowadays. That list will tell you how much of which nutrient you are getting with that product.

3. PROTEIN

Protein is a complex combination of amino acids and it makes up 17 % of our body weight. Essential in the formation of new cells it is also used in the structure of bones, skin, hair and muscle and contributes to hormone and enzyme production, for example insulin which controls the body's blood sugar levels.

Foods which are high in protein are lean meat, fish, other seafoods, cheese, eggs, yoghurt and milk. Vegetable foods also have a relatively high protein content. These are things such as lentils, beans, peas, nuts, seeds, grain and soya products such as tofu.

4. VITAMINS

In order for the protein, carbohydrates and fats to work properly in your body, you must have a good supply of the right vitamins. Here is a list of what each vitamin does to contribute to your physical well-being:

VITAMIN	Where to find it	What it does
A	Milk, dairy foods, oily fish, cod and halibut liver oil, carrots, root vegetables, sweet potatoes, spinach, apricots.	Promotes healthy eyes 'anti-infection vitamin' Helps growth and repairs tissues
B1	Wholemeal bread, brown rice, pulses yeast extract, cornflakes, meat, peanuts, bran.	Vital to the metabolism of carbohydrates Promotes growth Improves brain and nerve function
B2	Fish, eggs, milk, yeast.	Promotes growth and reproduction, healthy eyes, skin, nails and hair
B3	Poultry, nuts, grains, fish, eggs, liver, yeast. The body also makes its own.	Increases proper utilisation of food and aids maintenance of body tissues

THE PROBLEM OF WEIGHT

VITAMIN	Where to find it	What it does
B5	Grains, yeast, eggs, green vegetables, liver, molasses, brewer's yeast, chicken.	Assists adrenal gland, energy production and immune system
B6	Bananas, wheatgerm, turkey, yeast, eggs, wholegrain cereal, offal, beef, milk.	Promotes the production of red blood cells and antibodies, and vital for protein manufacture.
FOLIC ACID	Carrots, liver, kidneys, fish, cheese, whole wheat, offal, green vegetables	Important in the formation of red blood cells
B12	Meat, eggs, milk, cheese. Body also manufactures its own.	Promotes cell life, a healthy nervous system and the metabolism of iron
C	Green leafy vegetables, potatoes, fruits, berries.	Essential for many body functions, including healing wounds and diseases.
D	Manufactured by body itself from sunlight, fish and dairy foods.	Promotes proper use of calcium and phosphorous in the build up and maintenance of healthy bones and teeth.
E	Vegetable oils, milk, eggs, nuts, dark green vegetables.	Protects the circulatory system and cells.
K	Green vegetables, turnips, cereals, egg yolks, yoghurt, alfalfa, fish oils	Essential for blood clotting

As our modern food becomes increasingly refined, there is a great danger of us missing out on vital minerals as they are depleted in the refining processes.

Minerals help to store and distribute water and help to facilitate the chemical reactions that take place in your body and your brain. They also regulate muscle constriction. So make sure that you have enough of the following minerals in your diet.

So where are minerals found?

NOTE:

Excessive sodium intake can be harmful

TIP:

Beware of these sodium rich foods and use a salt substitute to flavour your food

CALCIUM:
Dairy products, peas, beans, potatoes, cauliflower, molasses, dried figs.

MAGNESIUM:
Dark green leafy vegetables, soya products, nuts and grains.

POTASSIUM:
Grains, fruit and vegetables

IRON
Liver, kidney, egg yolk, shellfish, vegetables, meat, fish, poultry, cereals.

ZINC
steak, chops, liver, egg yolk, wholewheat products, cereals, pulses, chicken, shellfish.

SODIUM (SALT)
Salty foods, such as bacon, ham, processed cheese, crisps and nuts, cornflakes, cheese biscuits, tinned soups, soy sauce, yeast extract (e.g. Marmite)

A HEALTHY BALANCE

To be healthy, you need the necessary nutrients in the correct balance in your diet. The different nutrients complement each other and work together to maintain your health. You must therefore eat a wide range of food to get all the nutrients you need - whilst being careful not to have excessive amounts of any individual nutrient. If you eat from each of the following groups of food each day you will achieve a reasonably balanced and healthy diet:

GROUP 1:	GROUP 2:	GROUP 3:	GROUP 4:
PROTEIN AND VITAMINS B12, A & D	COMPLEX CARBOHYDRATE (ENERGY), B VITAMINS. VITAMIN A, IRON, FIBRE	VITAMINS A, B1,B2, NIACIN, FOLIC ACID, VITAMIN C, IRON MAGNESIUM, POTASSIUM	PROTEIN, CALCIUM, VITAMINS A, B1, B12, D.
MEAT FISH POULTRY EGGS CHEESE NUTS PULSES	GRAINS BREAD CEREALS PASTA CARROTS STARCHY VEGETABLES (corn, potatoes)	LEAFY VEGETABLES FRUIT	MILK YOGHURT CHEESE

If you make up your meals using items from each of these groups, you will achieve a healthy balanced diet which is low in fat and sugar.

BEING SLIM IS A SKILL

Lifeguide expert Colin Rose, author of *The Mind and Body Diet*, believes fully that the mind is as crucial to weight loss as eating the right foods. Colin is a member of the British Association for the Advancement of Science and

has researched and reported on several major nutritional and psychological innovations. He is co-founder of Uni-Vite Nutrition and his weight loss programme has an international market. Studies show that with conventional weight loss programmes, 90% of those who have lost weight put some if not all the weight back on again within a short time. We are told constantly that if we want to lose weight, we must cut down on our calorific intake and increase our levels of exercise. And this is perfectly true. But what we are not told is that the right mental attitude towards weight loss is vital - without it, most of us will fail to maintain our weight loss.

MIND AND BODY DIET

Four key phrases make up the basis of Colin Rose's weight loss theories:-

1. **'Forget dieting as an issue in your life forever.'**
2. **'Staying slim is a skill.'**
3. **'50% of slimming is to do with achieving the right positive mental attitude'**
4. **'Successful slimming has little or nothing to do with will power. It has everything to do with wanting to be slim more than you want to eat unnecessarily.'**

Radical stuff, isn't it? But he is right. To 'forget dieting as an issue' avoids the vicious circle I described earlier which results from 'going on a diet' and relying on short term practical solutions to your weight problem. Maintaining your weight loss is a problem which is separate from the problem of losing weight initially. It *is* a skill. But it is one which you can acquire. A positive mental attitude is the key to achieving most things in life - including weight loss.

THE PROBLEM WITH CONVENTIONAL DIETS

Firstly, in conventional weight loss diets the emphasis is too much on **negatives**. For instance, don't do this, don't eat that. Secondly, most conventional weight loss diets are based around self-denial. As such, you feel deprived and therefore uncomfortable. Your subconscious will naturally resist any discomfort - one of our basic human instincts is to avoid pain and be comfortable. Pretty soon you will be unable to resist that discomfort, you will rebel and you will binge.

Thirdly, there is always a conflict with a conventional weight loss diet between the conscious mind and the subconscious mind. Your conscious mind knows that reducing the amount of food you eat will enable you to lose weight. Meanwhile your subconscious mind feels deprived of the necessary nutrition. The subconscious mind is programmed to know that if you don't get the right nutrition, you will eventually die. As such, your subconscious mind will be telling you to eat, whilst your conscious mind is denying that urge. When your conscious and subconscious conflict in this way, the subconscious will always win as we saw in Chapter One.

'All things must be mentally accomplished before they are physically accomplished'

Colin Rose's success in helping people to lose weight and maintain the weight loss long term is based on recognising the combined importance of three key areas: Mind-Body-Motivation

THE MIND

Forget the negative - 'losing weight'
Concentrate on the positive - 'becoming slim'

If your mind is full of positives, you are heading for success. If your mind is full of negatives, you are heading for failure.

Part of acquiring the skill to be slim means that you must ensure that there is no conflict between your conscious and subconscious minds - or the 'inner' and 'outer' selves as Colin Rose calls them. We've already established that you can control your subconscious thoughts. There are two things you can do to change the subconscious negatives into positives.

1. **Imagine yourself slim**. Picture yourself as a slim person, walking around the shops, or at work. Imagination is stronger than will-power. 'A slim mind creates a slim body'. It is important to visualise yourself slim in specific everyday situations.

2. **Accept responsibility for your weight loss**. You are in control of your weight loss. The 'diet' isn't doing it for you. You are doing it. You have made the decision to become a slim person. You make the decision to change your eating plan and to adapt it to fit your lifestyle. You are in control. It is your decision to be slim.

The repetition of conscious positive statements will affect your subconscious assumptions which affect your behaviour. So repeat the following statement 10 times when you wake up in the morning; 10 times during the day and 10 times just before you go to sleep:*'I am a slim person. I am in control of what I put into my body'*.
Don't be put off by the simplicity of these statements. Short and simple positive messages will take root in your subconscious and will become the reality. Try it, and you'll see that it works. The repetition of positive beliefs

enables you to eradicate the deep-rooted negative thoughts that you currently have about yourself and about your ability to succeed.

GOAL SETTING WORKS

REMEMBER:

Set realistic goals!

A crucial part of your mental preparation for the new and slim you is to set a realistic goal. Write it down. State your age, height, current weight, your goal weight, and a date by which you hope to have achieved your goal.

Being realistic about what you can achieve within a certain amount of time is vital. If you decide you want to lose three stone (19.5 kg) in six weeks, you will probably fail. This could destroy all the new positive thoughts and behaviour. If you have weight to lose, aim for 3-4 lb (1.5 kg) per week at the very most. So if you have a stone (6.35 kg) to lose, allow enough time for you to achieve that goal realistically. For instance:

Date	Age	Height	Current Weight	Goal Weight	Goal Date
1.3.91	29	5'6"	10 st 7 lb	9 st 7 lb	7.4.91.
		(1.68 m)	(66.5 kg)	(60.5 kg)	

Set out your record sheet in this way.

DECIDING TO BE MOTIVATED

You might find it easier to only set yourself short term goals and move from one to the next. So instead of setting a goal date of six months, set yourself a weekly or a monthly goal instead. The sense of achievement will be greater and more immediate.

THE PROBLEM OF WEIGHT

You will lose weight if you have the right motivation. If you see the benefits of losing weight as outweighing the disadvantages, you will lose weight.
Draw up a list like the one below

The Benefits of Being Slim	The Costs of Being Slim
Feel healthier	Deal with my sexuality
	Have to deal with problems

It may seem surprising to you that there could be any disadvantages to being slim, but there are. People will treat you differently when you are slim. You will have to change your lifestyle. You may have to change your behaviour. You will have a new sexual identity that may be difficult to cope with. To use an extreme example, psychologists believe that one of the main reasons why some very young girls develop anorexia nervosa is because they cannot cope with becoming a woman. Their developing sexual identity is squashed by their illness - as the girl literally starves herself, becoming thinner and thinner, her periods stop and she resumes her childish identity once more. She doesn't want the responsibility of sexuality and of dealing with the decisions and behaviour that adulthood brings with it. Similarly, making yourself very fat can achieve the same results. If you are very fat you feel unattractive. If you feel unattractive and have low self-esteem, other people will treat you as such. You can hide from your responsibilities as a sexual person.

BECOMING SLIM WON'T SOLVE ALL YOUR PROBLEMS

Many of the letters we received when making the *Lifeguide* series for television were from women who desperately wanted help in becoming slim. Here is a typical letter to illustrate this point:

Dear Lifeguide,

I have a wonderful home, terrific husband and great kids. I know I should be happy but I'm not. I'm three stone [19.5kg] overweight and I need your help to lose it, because I know my life would be okay if I could be slim. I feel very depressed all the time and I know my family is getting fed up with me. My doctor has prescribed tranquilisers but they don't seem to be helping. I feel very fat and ugly and so would appreciate your help in losing this weight.

Yours sincerely

The main focus of this letter is on the woman's weight problem. It is clear that her life isn't as she would like it to be and she is consequently feeling very down. She believes that by losing weight, all her other problems would disappear. But this isn't necessarily true. Yes, we can help her to lose weight. But what happens when she has lost the weight and she's still unhappy? Blaming your feelings on being fat is very counter-productive. If you lose that weight, you will then have to take responsibility for your other feelings.

Try to examine why you are overweight. Confront your true feelings. Do you eat when you're feeling depressed, for instance? If you do, then you need to tackle the depression first, rather than the weight. Why are you feeling depressed? What can you do to stop feeling like this? If you have these feelings and you deal with the weight problem first, those feelings will still be there after the extra weight has gone. Get to know the real you, don't push problems to the back of your mind. Confront your feelings, and gain control of your life.

And how is your self-esteem? If you cherish something, you take care of it. If you cherish yourself, you take care of yourself. Overeating and becoming fat has no connection with cherishing yourself. If you like yourself, then others will too. You are a worthwhile person and, as such, your body is worth taking care of. The fact is if you are very overweight you are not very healthy. If you're not healthy, your body won't work properly. You are in control of what you do with your body. Learn to like yourself and learn to like your body.

At *Lifeguide* we believe that positive thinking is the key to achieving most goals in life. Becoming slim is no exception. So now that you've read about the theories of becoming slim, here's some of the practical advice that our viewers have found so helpful throughout the series:

ASSESS YOUR DIET

Record every single thing that you eat over a period of three days on a large sheet of paper. That means every chocolate biscuit, every piece of cheese, every cup of coffee, every spoonful of sugar. Be very honest with yourself - and if you're given to sneaking downstairs in the middle of the night for a quick snack, write that down too.

After three days, look at the list and see where you can make improvements to your diet. If you take two spoonfuls of sugar in your tea and coffee, for instance, substitute low calorie sweetener instead. It's much easier to analyse your diet when the facts are written down - you may have noticed, for instance, that most of your meals consist of fatty meat and fried foods. Substitute those with fresh vegetables and lean meat.

It is useful to write down when you are more prone to overeating - is it for instance when you have a problem to cope with, or when you've had a row with your partner, or when things don't go right at work. Perhaps you eat when you're bored or feeling lonely. If you can pinpoint these patterns of eating, you can do something about it. You can reverse these habits. You can find another habit to replace the eating - exercise, writing, doing jobs around the house, seeing friends. Anything at all which is going to take your attention away from the fridge or the biscuit tin! Above all, get to know , the reason why you eat and the times when you are feeling the most vulnerable.

REMEMBER

Your eating habits must reflect and complement your lifestyle.

Armed with the knowledge of what is required for your healthy balanced diet, and your new positive mental approach to yourself and your body, make changes to your current diet. With the right amount and kind of proteins, carbohydrates, fats, vitamins and minerals you will very quickly feel and see the difference. Instead of feeling full and sluggish after a meal, for instance, you will notice that you feel refreshed and ready for whatever task lies ahead.

DR CHRIS STEELE'S FAT FAREWELL DIET

A. WHAT TO EAT

* *Where amounts are not stipulated, any amount of that item is allowed.*
* *Where fish is mentioned, any fish can be eaten except for tinned fish in oil. Tinned fish in brine is allowed.*
* *Where meat is mentioned, any meat without the fat is acceptable. Sausage meats are not allowed*

BREAKFAST

1. Single fresh fruit- I apple or I orange etc. or a glass of fruit juice.
2. One egg with one slice of brown toast or one average helping of unsweetened cereal.
3. Tea or coffee - any amount.

LUNCH

1. Low calorie soup - one serving.
2. Lean meat - any amount.
3. Mixed salad - any amount. (Meat and salad can be taken as a sandwich with two slices of wholemeal bread.)
4. Single fresh fruit - I apple or I orange etc.
5. Tea or coffee - any amount.

EVENING MEAL

1. Meat of your choice - any amount or Fish of your choice.
2. Two fresh vegetables - any amount.
3. One baked potato. or small helping of boiled potatoes or small helping of boiled rice or small helping of pasta.
4. Fresh fruit or - very low fat fruit yoghurt.
5. Tea or coffee - any amount

SNACKS - Ideally no eating between meals!

* If tempted nibble on raw carrots, celery, radishes, pickled onions or melon.
* If thirsty use low calorie soft drink, Bovril, Oxo, Marmite or mineral waters. Tea or coffee are allowed using low calorie sweeteners and no more than the daily allowance of milk.

FORBIDDEN FOODS

* Avoid sweets, sugar, chocolate, jam, cakes, pastry, biscuits.
* Avoid fat: eg. fat on meat, skin on poultry, butter, cream.
* Avoid all fried foods.
* Avoid thick soups, thick sauces, mayonnaise.
* Avoid alcohol: If alcohol must be taken restrict intake. Drink dry wines instead of sweet wines. In terms of calories 2 glasses of dry wine = I pint of beer or I single whisky.

LIFEGUIDE GROUPS

INSTEAD OF	TAKE
Sugar	Low calorie sweeteners
Milk	Semi-skimmed milk- I pint per day allowed
White bread	Wholemeal bread - 3 slices per day allowed
Cheese	Cottage cheese
Butter	Low-fat spreads - used sparingly
Soft dri nks	Low calorie drinks - eg. One-Cal
Fried foods	Grilled, poached, baked, boiled or steamed
Bananas	Any other fresh fruit

CAROL : LIFEGUIDE MEMBER

Carol is 45. She has been married but is now divorced, and is a mother and grandmother. When Carol came to the first discussion group, she was particularly quiet. It was clear at the beginning that if anyone didn't feel comfortable talking then they should do just what they wanted and listen. Nobody in the group minded this (immediately there was an atmosphere of camaraderie and mutual support and understanding) and the discussion continued. People talked honestly of their experiences of depression and lack of confidence and of their dreams and ambitions. Carol listened intently but still didn't speak.

Just before the end of the discussion, Carol stood up and spoke to the rest of the group. She said that because she was so lacking in confidence, speaking to any number of people had seemed impossible for her, but by listening to the other women talking about their problems she had felt inspired by the warmth and support, so much so that she wanted everyone to know how much better she felt for having come along. It was clearly very difficult for Carol to stand up and say this, but what she said hit home with everyone. She had articulated the feeling of support and strength that everyone was feeling at the end of the two-hour discussion but that no one had identified directly.

Carol was out of work when she joined Lifeguide. She lacked self-esteem and so felt unable to have a go at life and achieve anything. She had a problem with her weight which she believed was affecting her potential in the job market. She didn't want to go out; social events and interviews were a nightmare for her as she was convinced that she was being judged on the fact that she was overweight. She believed she was worthless and that others thought she was too. Carol was married for 20 years. Talking in the group she stated that during her marriage she had been physically abused by her husband and she told us that her weight problem began when she was married. Because she did not receive love or affection from her husband, she started to eat to comfort herself. Most of the time that she was being beaten, Carol had believed that she deserved to be hit. She believed that as a person she had little value and that she was responsible for driving her husband to violence. It took 12 years for Carol to gather enough confidence to leave the marriage. She is only now slowly regaining the lost confidence to make herself feel better. Joining Lifeguide and speaking at the group were her first positive steps to a happier lifestyle.

Within a month of joining Lifeguide Carol got a job as a nursery nurse. A month ago she was promoted to Deputy Officer-in-Charge at the nursery. She looks and feels great. She has lost some weight, but feels that is not the important thing; rather, life is getting better and better all the time because her mental attitude has changed. She has begun to believe that she can achieve the things she wants. She has decided to take charge of her life and make things happen for her. Carol says, 'Because of joining Lifeguide and talking to the other women, I have gained so much more confidence. I feel better about myself as a whole and I feel more positive about the future.'

CHAPTER THREE

FEELING FIT

FEELING FIT

Does the thought of exercising conjure up images of tall slim women in fancy leotards and headbands doing high energy aerobics? And are you so intimidated by the thought of this image that you dismiss any ideas you may have had about taking up some form of exercise? We found this to be the case with many of the women we talked to on *Lifeguide*. Many thought that exercise was the prerogative of the young and the slim.

You can banish these images forever; if exercising in public fills you with horror, you can do it at home on your own or with a friend. And forget those nightmare images of bright pink co-ordinating leotards - all you need are loose-fitting clothes which allow you to move freely and comfortably whilst you exercise.

Before we go any further, let's run through the benefits of exercise and the positive effects it can have on your life:

1. Exercise burns off calories
2. Exercise helps to lower blood pressure and cholesterol levels - thereby helping to guard against heart disease.
3. Exercise increases your metabolic rate and this is not only just during the time you are exercising. If you exercise, the increased rate of metabolism will last for several hours after you have finished exercising. This means that you will burn more calories.
4. Exercise is a mechanism for lowering your body's 'set point'; Colin Rose explains that when your body has been a certain weight for a length of time, that weight becomes your body's 'set point'. The body has become used to that weight. As such your body fights to defend this weight. So when you lose weight, your

body will want to adjust to the original higher weight.
Exercise seems to be the only way you can change
and lower your set point. If you exercise, the body
will accept your new lower weight as natural and
will adjust to it. So it is easier to maintain your
weight loss if you exercise.

5. Exercise helps to control your appetite; it increases the
level of a hormone called noradrenaline in your blood
to five times the normal level and increases adrenaline
levels by 2-3 times. Noradrenaline is the hormone
which inhibits your hunger and raises your metabolic
rate. And adrenaline does the same thing. Adrenaline
also helps to move fat from the fat cells into the blood
to be burnt off. Exercise also increases the level of
another hormone serotonin which - in high levels -
'switches off' your hunger.

REMEMBER:

*Metabolic rate
refers to the rate
at which you
burn off calories.*

Regular exercise also releases natural chemicals in your
brain called opiates which have the pleasing effect of
making you feel happy. All in all, then, exercise makes you
feel both physically and psychologically better, and if you
are losing weight, you can do so more easily by
exercising.

REMEMBER **Before you start any exercise programme consult your GP
first if you have any concerns about your health or fitness**

Exercise should be a part of your lifestyle whatever your
age. And it is vital that you choose a form of exercise that
you enjoy; there are many different ways of exercising
and if you hate running, try swimming instead. If you try
to persevere with something you don't like, you will see
exercise as a negative activity. But the truth is that you
can really enjoy exercising.

Our *Lifeguide* expert on fitness is Dr John Williams of the Department of Movement Science and Physical Education at the University of Liverpool, and co-director of the Body-Check Health and Fitness Consultancy. Dr Williams has been actively involved in sport and exercise for nearly forty years and has himself been a junior representative athlete and games player, a track athlete and team manager with the Royal Air Force. He has some 75 scientific papers and conference presentations to his credit with specialist research interests in movement control and the perception of effort.

I'm going to hand over to Dr Williams as he offers not only the scientific evidence of benefits of exercise and fitness, but also provides a check which you can do to assess your own level of fitness.

EXERCISE FOR HEALTHY FITNESS
BY *LIFEGUIDE* EXPERT DR. JOHN WILLIAMS

There seems to be a great interest in both 'health' and 'fitness' these days. Not so long ago the word health was linked with illness. When a person became ill they went to their doctor who helped them get better. Similarly, the term fitness was the concern of competitive athletes who engaged in punishing workouts in order to achieve better performances in their chosen sport. Times have changed! Nowadays, there is a much greater public awareness of habits and behaviours which can lead to illness. Smoking and poor diet are good examples. We are also aware of activities which can promote wellness, such as eating wisely and taking regular exercise. Many people are altering formerly unquestioned habits to prevent illness.

Similarly, there has been an upsurge of interest in becoming 'fit', not necessarily to enhance performance in a particular sport but more because of the realisation that improvements in physical proficiency can be achieved by all of us and when the challenge of vigorous exercise is taken, we feel better and are healthier as a result of being involved.

For some years I have been involved with a heath-related fitness assessment programme called 'Body-Check'. The procedure examines five factors which research has shown to be associated with systemic illnesses such as coronary heart disease. These are blood pressure, total blood cholesterol level, body composition (ratio of fat to lean tissue), lung function, and aerobic fitness (ability of heart and lungs to deliver oxygen to the muscles). Many men and women of all ages have been involved. The final part of the procedure is a thorough counselling session at which the results of the assessments are explained and some advice on how to proceed is offered. After meeting many people on this programme and in the general course of my work in the health sciences and physical education over many years, I and colleagues have found that people of all ages and backgrounds have a serious interest in both their own health and that of their families and, furthermore, believe that some form of regular physical activity would contribute to their overall well being. Also, they are prepared to take action to become healthier and this includes becoming fitter. However, it is quite plain that before taking action they want reliable information about their current health and fitness. In particular they want to be better informed about the role of exercise in health, what they should do and how they should go about it. This chapter of the *Lifeguide* book systematically addresses these matters. Sections are presented on the benefits of exercise, assessment of fitness using a self-rating scale, an explanation of the various components of fitness, advice or the management of exercise and a menu of activities which the reader uses to design a basic exercise programme.

BENEFITS OF EXERCISE

The beneficial effects upon health brought about by taking regular exercise in people of all ages and backgrounds are now well established. For some time, the effects of 'training' which periodically demands that the heart and lungs (cardio-respiratory system) or the muscles and joints (musculo-skeletal system) work harder than usual has beer well documented by studies of competitive athletes and people who were already physically fit and participating in activities such as distance running, swimming and cycling. Training results in radical changes in the capacity of the heart to send blood to the working muscles, the capacity of the blood to carry the vital 'nutrient' oxygen, and the ability of the system to extract the oxygen required for relatively intense and sustained activity to be carried out. Improvements in strength and flexibility (range of movement at the joints of the skeleton) can also be achieved. By engaging in suitably designed exercise programmes, positive physical improvements of this kind are now known to be attainable by virtually everyone. Although the evidence is more difficult to assess at present, there are some reports that exercise may also exert a beneficial influence on both psychological well being and mental health.

An alternative proposal currently being carefully studied by those interested in the promotion of wellness is the possibility that 'lack of training' which accompanies lifestyle of a sedentary nature in conjunction with some unhealthy habits and behaviours could somehow be connected with illness in the very same system that responds so positively when exercised. This has come about mainly as the result of a quest to prevent disability and death from coronary heart disease (CHD) which is so prevalent in many advanced industrial societies. It is an ironic fact that whereas general conditions of life are improving and certain diseases are well under control, there remains a very high incidence of diseases of the heart and blood vessels. About half of all deaths in the UK are the result of coronary heart or artery disease.

A strong association between high levels of physical activity and low incidence of coronary heart disease has now been confirmed. Research indicates that the risk reduction is directly related to the time spent on vigorous physical activity per week. A number of studies have shown that lack of activity can be as sizeable a coronary heart disease risk factor as high blood pressure (hypertension), high levels of blood cholesterol (hypercholesterolaemia) or cigarette smoking.

Exercise which is vigorous, regular and current appears to reduce the risk of suffering a heart attack by 50%. Vigorous activity has been defined as that which requires an energy expenditure of 7.5 kcals/minute (12 minutes per mile pace for brisk walk or jogging) and is maintained for at least 3 periods of 20 minutes per week. Ensuring that such exercise is a regular part of current lifestyle is critical as a history of participation in physical activity and sports in early adult life does not appear to sustain a protective effect. It should be noted that whereas the effects of training take effect in some ten to fourteen days, inactivity works in the opposite direction!

The mechanisms by which exercise may provide a protective effect include beneficial alterations in lipid (fat) metabolism, blood clotting factors and arterial blood pressure. Regular, vigorous exercise improves the ratio of high density lipids (HDL) (beneficial within the system) to low density lipids (LDL) (detrimental to the system). Overall, cholesterol levels may also decrease. These changes are consistent with a lower rate of deposition of fatty material on arterial blood vessels which reduces the risk of CHD.

Moderate rhythmic, exercise which involves the large muscle groups of the body brings about increased fibrinolytic activity and reduced platelet aggregation. This protects against blood clot formation. If exercise is taken regularly this effect may be of longer term benefit against the damaging effects of thromboses. It has been demonstrated that hypertension (high blood pressure: values of above 140/90 mm Hg), often termed 'the silent killer', can be lowered by moderately intense, rhythmic exercise. It is possible that the rise in blood pressure with age which is common in many advanced industrial societies may be modulated to some extent by regular exercise.

If you don't take regular exercise of the kind just mentioned and the rest of what was said fails to convince you that you should take action then it is probably not worth reading any further!

WHAT IS FITNESS?

Fitness is a much used word in everyday conversation which requires explanation. Generally speaking, a person is fit if they are in sound athletic condition. In practice it seems reasonable to say that a person can be considered fit if he or she is able to cope satisfactorily with the non-leisure demands of life and still have sufficient energy to participate in active leisure pursuits. Also, it is worth adding that even in a highly mechanised and automated society there are occasions when all of us are called upon to use our bodies in a vigorous manner. To be ready to cope with such situations is another way of considering the term fitness.

The term 'fitness' can be defined in a variety of ways. In the present context it is used to mean physiological (and, possibly, psychological) changes which take place in an individual as a result of involvement in exercise which is compatible with healthful living. I believe that the moderate stresses that appropriately selected vigorous exercise exerts on both the body's muscles and joints, heart and lungs have a positive and beneficial influence on health in people of all ages. Such activity counteracts negative influences and adaptations which have resulted from relatively recent social and technological innovations and changes. Detail on the components of fitness will be provided later in the section on exercise management. To conclude, it seems worth stating that it is quite possible to be fit but not healthy and healthy but not fit. An attainable goal for all of us could be to reach and maintain a state of 'healthy fitness'. This does not mean that we have to enter a programme of 'training' in the manner of a competitive athlete but rather to incorporate appropriate and sensibly vigorous exercise into our lives along side the many other activities that most of us have to do. This should ensure that our bodily systems, which are designed for movement, are maintained in good condition and will serve us well when needed.

ASSESSING YOUR OWN FITNESS LEVEL

Fitness can be assessed at various levels. At the most detailed level this would require a person to undergo a series of tests in a fully equipped, accredited, exercise physiology laboratory. The tests would involve a searching analysis of the response of a person's heart and lungs, muscles and joints when performing standard tasks requiring graded effort. Interpretation of the results of such a procedure demands professional training and experience in Exercise Science. There are a number of these facilities in Britain. In the main these are used either to test competitive athletes or to manage the rehabilitation of patients who have been ill with coronary disease. Recently, there has been a noticeable increase in the number of community leisure centres and health clubs offering fitness assessments. The quality of the services offered and the usefulness of the information provided to the clientele has not been determined.

Plainly, laboratory-based fitness testing is not available to most people and is probably not necessary except in special circumstances. One of the reasons for this is that humans already possess a very good system for sensing physical effort. They use it all the time. All of us have experienced vigorous physical work and have sensed whether we were able to continue or had to stop and rest. In fact, if asked the question 'How fit are you?' most people could provide a reasonably accurate estimate because of recent experience with tasks which require some effort such as walking up a flight of stairs or having to run to catch a bus. With a little bit of fine tuning we can 'listen' to our own effort sense to assess our physical fitness. Also, we can use this sense to gauge the intensity of our efforts when we are actually exercising.

Now you can assess your own level of fitness by rating how you would feel and cope if you had to use your body vigorously in a set of situations of which virtually all of us have recent experience.

Set out here is a rating scale. This is based on a more comprehensive scale which can be found in most exercise testing laboratories. A little time spent studying this device should help you to organise the feelings of effort or strain that we all experience when we use our bodies to do physical work. The numbers on the scale are linked with expressions of effort. Below the scale short descriptions of the effort involved at each point on the scale are provided. You will note that the larger the number on the scale, the greater the effort, strain or exertion. Given below the rating scale and its descriptions are sets of everyday situations which require physical exertion. Most of these situations have been experienced recently and we know the effort involved.

Effort sense rating scale (ESRS)

0 *minimal effort/strain*

I *Quite easy*

2 *Somewhat hard*

3 *Quite hard*

4 *Maximal effort/strain*

0. Would require hardly any effort at all; completely manageable.

I. Would require some effort; could be managed quite easily.

2. Would be quite hard; could be done but not managed easily. Five to ten minutes recovery required before ready to do other things.

3. Would be very tiring and affect anything that had to be done during the next half hour.

4. Would be exhausting and take more than a half hour to recover and carry out normal activities.

To assess your fitness you should read the situations, select TWO from Set A and TWO from Set B as they relate to your recent experience then rate yourself with the aid of the scale. Add up your ratings and refer to the FITNESS CATEGORIES which are provided below.

OVERALL FITNESS SCORE...................

FITNESS CATEGORIES

Score	Description
0-8	Very acceptable level of physical fitness. Either currently involved in an appropriate exercise programme or have a 'naturally' very sound system.
9-11	Borderline status. Perhaps in the early stages of an exercise programme and adapting toward the acceptable zone or losing fitness and moving the wrong way.
12-16	Low level of fitness in a system which has some difficulty in coping with challenges or emergencies. Suitable exercise programme should be followed which will lead to adaptations to enable coping.

SITUATIONS REQUIRING EFFORT
SET A   **Rating....**

1. You have to lift a small child, bag of groceries, medium size suitcase or similar load and walk briskly up 10 to 15 stairs.

2. You have to run 40 to 50 metres to catch a bus or train that you mustn't miss.

3. You and another person help push a friend's car to start it. This takes one effort of about 20 to 30 metres constant pushing.

4. A young relative (5 to 10 years old) challenges you to race to a selected point and back. Across the pool and back swimming (20 to 30 metres) or to the end of the road and back running (70 to 80 metres). You can't turn down the challenge and don't want to be beaten!

SET B

1. You have to meet a child from school. You have no mechanical transport. The school is 10 to 12 minutes brisk walk away. You have to walk/run to be there on time.

2. You have a lively young dog which slips its lead. It may run on to a busy road. You have to chase it for several minutes to retrieve it.

3. Your car runs out of petrol some half a mile (804.6 metres) from a petrol station and you have an important appointment to keep. You decide to hurry (run/walk) to get the petrol.

4. You're in the park with a young relative and friends and they challenge you to a race around the park perimeter. It is much bigger than a regular running track. It takes the children 10 minutes continuous running to get around. You can't refuse!

EXERCISE MANAGEMENT

The process of exercise management consists of deciding upon personal fitness goals, selecting appropriate activities, designing an exercise programme then fitting the programme into the rhythm of daily life. Once things are underway it is a good idea to evaluate the effects of the programme in relation to the goals that were originally set and, if necessary, make adjustments. This gives your programme purpose and direction. This section helps you with this process and is where the real action begins.

If you have decided that exercise is for you but have some reservations because of your previous health record or similar reason then it is a good idea to talk with your GP, explain your intentions and take advice.

The next step is to obtain an estimate of your current fitness. If you have a particular wish to undergo an exercise testing procedure then you will need to make an appointment with an organisation that offers such a service. There is no national directory which tells where these services are available. Local enquiries at sport centres and colleges or universities with sport science and/or physical education departments should be able to help. Some GPs and hospitals are beginning to offer 'wellness' assessments. Also, there are some private consultancies, and membership of BUPA offers exercise testing. Ensure that you check on the qualifications of those offering the service and expect to pay a fee (anywhere between £10 at the local Sport Centre to £150 with BUPA). As explained previously, most people merely wish to embark on a straightforward exercise programme with the goal of attaining healthy fitness. An honest self-assessment of the kind you did in the previous section is quite adequate.

DESIGNING AN EXERCISE PROGRAMME

Regular participation plays an important role in achieving and maintaining physical fitness, you should plan when and how often you will be able to exercise. Try to fit the sessions of exercise into a daily/weekly routine. Remember, 'little and often' is far better than a 'really tough workout' once in a while. Everyone can find time for sufficient exercise to achieve a good level of healthy fitness if they believe exercise commands a high enough priority in their life as a whole. To design a programme a little knowledge is required about the various aspects of fitness (these will be referred to as 'components'), the means by which the desired level of fitness is to be achieved (called here the 'agents'), and the types of activity (called the 'menu') used to achieve the goal of healthy fitness. These three aspects will be explained briefly and then you will be ready to design your own programme and get going.

COMPONENTS OF FITNESS

Improved fitness takes place following positive changes in the following health-related components:

Stamina

This determines endurance or stamina for work lasting longer than 5 minutes and is concerned with the ability of the heart and lungs to deliver oxygen to the muscles so that you can keep moving. The best examples of this are seen in elite distance runners who have developed the capability perform at a some 80 per cent or more of their maximum capacity for between 30 minutes and 2 hours. The technical term for this is aerobic capacity. Experience indicates that many people are vulnerable in this area. The good news is that all of us are able to readily improve our aerobic capacity.

Strength

This refers to the ability of muscles to generate tension and, thus, to provide forceful contractions. All of us require a reasonably strong system both to maintain an erect posture, and to move about and complete everyday tasks. There are different kinds of strength. For example there is the 'explosive' version whereby heavy a load is moved in a brief period of time (lifting a heavy box of groceries into the boot of a car) and the 'dynamic' version in which repeated, vigorous bodily movements are required for as long as a minute (e.g. sprinting). The technical term for the latter type is anaerobic capacity. This means that we use sources of energy which are available within our system to get the work done. Short sharp bursts of activity leave us panting for breath which is the body's way of repaying the debt which the work caused and getting the system back in balance.

Suppleness

This refers to the range of movement in the various joint complexes of the body (static) and the ease of such movement (dynamic). As with strength, reasonable levels of suppleness can be achieved and maintained with a programme of simple exercises.

A lowering of capability in all of the above components results from sedentary life style but immediate positive adaptation occurs from involvement in a properly designed exercise programme which should contain a balance of activities chosen to develop all of these elements which are sometimes referred to as the 3 S's.

The Agents of Fitness

Three change agents, operating in combination, act to adapt the fitness components mentioned above. These are:

FREQUENCY: how often you exercise.
DURATION: how long you exercise.
INTENSITY: how hard you exercise.
THE DECISION IS YOURS !

Whatever you decide will be based on current fitness level, your personal fitness goals, availability of time, etc. No hard and fast rules can be applied because of individual variations.

A general recommendation is frequency: 3 sessions per week; duration: 20-30 minutes incorporating activities relating to all of the above components in each session, with a bias toward stamina work (15-20) mins; intensity: level 2 on the Effort Sense Rating Scale would be a reasonable objective to be reached in a period of 3-4 months (90-100 sessions). The intensity level is the most difficult to judge and this is why you were introduced to the effort rating scale earlier. It should be used during exercise to help judge the correct intensity. Clearly, duration and intensity are linked. At the beginning of your programme you will only be able to sustain level 2 for a few minutes. As you persist with the programme you will find that you will be able to keep going at that level for a greater length of time. It is up to you if you eventually go beyond the recommended limit for the stamina section of a session but 20 minutes at level 2 is sufficient for most people to maintain a sound level of healthy fitness. It is recommended that you are patient and don't try to progress too quickly. Also, try not to drop to level 1 or stray into level 3 too often.

A menu of activities which can be used to achieve fitness goals related to the components of fitness are set out below. But first a few cautions before you begin exercise:

~ You are advised not to exercise if suffering from cold/influenza or recovering from these conditions; it is better to wait until a full recovery has been made. Recall that if there are aspects of your medical history which concern you talk with your GP before you begin your exercise programme.

~ You should understand and adhere to any safety advice associated with exercises. Your attention will be drawn to some exercises that should be avoided a little later. Also, it is advisable to exercise in the company of others (in twos or threes) if possible in case an accident occurs.

~ There is no need to buy expensive specialist clothing to wear when exercising. The most sensible and useful items are 'T' shirt and shorts, basic jogging suit and training shoes with good support and cushioning are all you need. A showerproof rain suit is a good idea if you are going outside in British weather.

Climatic conditions seriously influence everyone's performance so avoid exercising in extreme weather or other environmental conditions e.g. cold, heat and humidity, high winds, fog, polluted air etc.

Always take note of and abide by rules and safety advice when exercising particularly in specialist facilities such as gymnasia, swimming pools but also out on roads etc. If you are out in poor visibility ensure that you can be seen.

A BASIC EXERCISE PROGRAMME FOR ALL:

STRUCTURE OF AN EXERCISE SESSION

Every exercise session should consist of three parts. These are a **WARM-UP** (beginning), **MAIN SECTION**, **COOL-DOWN** (ending). The main section can either be geared to a single fitness component or consist of items which emphasise a range of components with a smaller amount of time spent on each. Examples for beginners are provided below for each section. In the main section advice is given on how a beginner might progress if regular exercise is maintained.

WARM-UP

The purpose of the warm-up is to prepare your body for the main section of the exercise session. This is essential and can help to avoid injury. Some 5 to 10 minutes should be spent on this activity which has the effect of raising body temperature, increasing blood flow to the muscles which will do the work, lubricating the joints for smoother action and alerting the nervous system for the more vigorous exercise to come.

The following warm-up is suggested. Keep your jogging suit on throughout.

1. Walk around steadily in a reasonable space (could be around the house) gradually progressing to brisk walking then to light jog. This could be done 'on the spot' if necessary. Do several short bouts (10-15 seconds) of easy walking, brisk walking and light jogging. Total time: 3 minutes. Rest 15-20 seconds.

2. Lie face down on floor, relax completely for a few seconds. Then stretch out, arms wide, legs wide, hold for few seconds relax. Repeat three times. Stand up, shake out then lie on back and stretch out as before. Repeat three times. Get up and walk or jog to another space. Stand feet astride, hands on hips. Turn head to right as far as possible (no strain) then left as far as possible. Repeat three times each way. Try to rest your head on your shoulder, three times each side. Next circle shoulders forwards three times followed by backwards three times. Turn whole upper body as far as possible to one side then the other(three each side). Pause for a moment then lie on back and raise knees alternately to chest (as far as possible) followed by feet to floor, 3-5 times up and back. Sit up, knees slightly bent and circle feet at ankles alternately clockwise and anti-clockwise. Total time: 5 minutes.

3. Alternate easy walk/brisk walk for 1 minute. Warm-up time 9-10 minutes. You are now ready for the main section.

There is a saying amongst athletes that 'one person's warm up is another's workout!' If you are seriously out of condition the warm-up given could be your main session for as much as a couple of weeks (even longer) before you are ready to take on more intensive exercise. Your own sense of the effort involved will tell you when it is time for more.

MAIN SECTION

This is the part of the exercise session in which improved stamina, strength, and suppleness can be achieved if the activities are approached steadily with gradual progression. A menu of activities which can be used to bring about adaptations in the above named fitness components is presented below. Some advice is provided but you choose and, in effect, design your own programme. Remember, exercise is very much an individual prescription, take a cautious approach. Work to your own sense of effort rather than what someone else does or says.

STRENGTH AND SUPPLENESS

Before embarking on activities which develop stamina it is vital that a sound foundation of strength and suppleness is achieved. The most convenient, effective way for an individual to develop such a foundation is through stretching exercises. Select your activities from those shown in the section called '**STRETCHING**' which is provided below. These exercises cover all of the major joints and muscle groups in the body. Develop your own stretching routine and spend 50-60% of your main section exercise time doing these activities in the early phases of your exercise programme. This amount can be reduced to 10-15% after 3-4 weeks but a certain amount of stretching should be done within every session. Remember you should have warmed up before stretching. There are more advanced exercise systems for the development of strength and suppleness. These require quite high levels of physical proficiency and specialist tuition. It is doubtful whether exercise at this level is necessary for the attainment of healthy fitness.

STRETCHING

Observe the diagram for each stretch, read the instructions and copy what you see. Stretch slowly in a continuous movement. Hold the final position for 5-30 sec and repeat 3-10 times; increase the length of hold and the number of repetitions when you sense that you are ready. It will take about a 100 sessions to achieve the maximum hold time and repetitions. Avoid pain, keep to levels 2 to 3 on the effort sense scale, no less no more. Length of hold develops your strength. Gradual increase in the range of movement will improve suppleness. Exercises that you may have seen but should **avoid** are: Deep knee bends (squats), lateral/medial movements of the knee (sideways). You should keep the feet flat on the floor when exercising in the standing position. Knees should be slightly flexed (bent) when touching toes from standing or sitting-up. Activities which you feel place an unusual strain on your lower back or neck are not advisable.

STRETCHING EXERCISES

A Procedure:

1. Stand comfortably, feet flat on the ground.

A
Brief description of exercise: shoulder stretching: standing position

Purpose of exercise: to stretch some of the muscles of the shoulder and chest

2. With the palm facing upward and the elbow fully extended (i.e. arm straight) and raised out to the side, move the arm slowly back, twisting the upper body slightly as you do. You should feel a stretching of the pectoralis major muscle, the large muscle of the chest between the shoulder and the sternum (breast bone).

3. Hold the final position for a few seconds, then return to the starting position.

4. Repeat with the other arm.

B Procedure:

1. Lie on your stomach with your chin resting on your hands (palms down).

2. Slowly push up your upper body by extending your arms at the elbows, thus extending the back. You should feel a stretching of the abdominal muscles. Hold this position for a few seconds.

3. Return to the prone starting position by bending at the elbows and lowering the upper body.

B

Brief description of exercise: half push-ups

Purpose of exercise: to stretch the muscles of the abdomen and chest

NOTE: Do not extend the back so as to create any pain or discomfort. Those with a history of back problems should be cautious with this and all other exercises involving back extension.

C Procedure:

1. Establish a sitting position with your knees bent comfortably, arms at your sides.

2. Slowly, with your chin tucked in and your back rounded as much as possible, rock backwards as far as comfortably possible (try to imagine the individual vertebrae of your spine as links in a chain and try to lay them down one at a time: this will help to keep your back curved). Do not roll all the way over in a full backward somersault. You should feel a stretching of the muscles of both the upper and lower back.

3. Hold the final position for a few seconds, then rock forward slowly, again with the back as curved as possible.

C

Brief description of exercise: back rock

Purpose of exercise: to increase the flexibility of some of the muscles attached to the vertebral column, particularly those of the lower back.

D Procedure:

1. Establish a solid, comfortable hands-and-knees position.

2. Begin by tucking your chin in, rocking your hips forward, and arching your back up. This position causes some books to refer to this exercise as the 'Mad Cat'!

3. Continue be returning to a straight back position, head in the starting position and hips rocked backward.

D

Brief description of exercise: arches and sags in the hands-and-knees position

Purpose of exercise: to strengthen and stretch the muscles of the back and abdomen

E Procedure:

1. Assume a supine position (i.e. lying on your back), with arms at your sides.

2. Place your fingers on the muscles of your chest and upper abdomen and lift your head up so that you can see the heels of your feet. With your fingers feel the rectus abdominus muscles contracting.

3. Hold this position for a few seconds, then relax an return to the starting position.

E

Brief description of the exercise: lying down and 'peaking up' by raising head off the floor

Purpose of exercise: to strengthen some of the muscles of the abdomen and chest

F Procedure:

1. Lie on your back with your knees bent, feet flat on the floor, and arms by your sides.

2. With your chin tucked in and your back as rounded as possible, roll up on one elbow into a sitting postion. **NOTE**: Do NOT 'jerk' yourself up with your back straight. Also, do NOT lock your feet under a chair or similar object. This brings muscles other than the abdominals (the hipflexors) into play and partially defeats the purpose of the exercise.

3. From the sitting position, again with the back rounded, return to the lying position by sitting back slowly, replacing the individual vertebrae of your spine on the floor one at a time.

F

Brief description of exercise: lying down, knees bent and rolling up to a starting position

Purpose of exercise: to strengthen the muscles of the abdomen

G Procedure:

1. Assume a supine position.

2. Flex one leg at the hip and knee and grasp that leg with both hands at the knee.

3. Pull your knee down toward your upper body until your upper leg touches your chest.

4. Hold this position for a few seconds, then return to starting position.

5. Repeat with other leg.

H Procedure:

1. Assume a prone position (i.e. on your stomach)

2. Bend one leg at the knee and reach back with one hand and grasp the foot of the bent leg.

3. Pull the foot down slightly and hold this position for a few seconds before relaxing. You should feel stretching of the muscles of the front thigh (the quadriceps).

4. Repeat with the other leg.

G

Brief description of exercise: lying on back, pulling knee down toward chest

Purpose of exercise: to stretch the gluteus maximus (buttocks)

I Procedure:

1. Stand with one foot placed about 2 ft (half a metre) in front of the other.

2. With the knee of the back leg straight, lean forward placing your weight on the front foot. You should feel

stretching in the large muscle of the calf (the gastromenemius). Hold this position for a few seconds.

3. While in this forward leaning position, bend the knee of the back leg, thus assuming a slight 'sitting' position. You should feel stretching of the other muscle of the calf (the soleus) slightly more toward the foot than the gastromemius. Hold this position for a few seconds then relax.

4. Switch leg positions and repeat for the other leg.

J Procedure:

1. Assume a solid standing position, feet flat about 3 ft (1 metre) apart with hands on hips.

2. Keeping feet flat on the floor, lean to one side bending the knee on that side while keeping the other leg straight. you should feel stretching of the muscles of the inside of the thigh of the straight leg (the adductors).

3. Hold this position for a few seconds, then repeat in the opposite direction.

K Procedure:

1. Lie on your back with your knees bent, feet flat on the floor, and arms at your sides.,

2. Lift your feet off the floor so that your lower legs are parallel to the floor and your knees are bent at an angle of 90°

3. Keeping your back flat on the floor and your feet and knees together, rotate your hips so that your legs move down to one side toward the floor.

H

Brief description of exercise: lying on stomach, pulling one foot at at time to rest on gluteus maximus

Purpose of exercise: To stretch the muscles of the front of the upper leg

I

Brief description of exercise: standing one leg in front of the other, leaning forward onto front foot, then sitting slightly

Purpose of exercise: to stretch the muscles of the calf

J

Brief description of exercise: standing, feet spread wide and flat on floor, hands on hips, leaning first to one side, then the other.

Purpose of exercise: to stretch the muscles of the inside of the upper leg

K

Brief description of exercise: hip rotations lying on the back

Purpose of exercise: to strengthen and improve the flexibility of some of the muscles of the hips

4. Hold your legs just above the floor, then return them to the upright position.

5. Repeat in the opposite direction.

STAMINA

Stamina is the ability to keep working at an activity for a relatively long time. The best way to achieve this is through an optimal balance of frequency, duration, and intensity doing the following activities:

Walking. . .Swimming. . .Cycling. . .Jogging. . .Running
Generally speaking these activities increase steadily in the demands placed on the system from left to right.

Walk/jogging/running are best done outdoors on traffic free roads or parkland. It is a good idea to map out a pleasant circuit of between 1 and 2 miles. Many sports centres now have treadmills if you prefer to stay indoors. Swimming is best in an appropriate aquatic facility preferably with a 'lane' cordoned off for continuous swimming or an area which allows reasonably uninterrupted activity.Cycling can be done outside, inside on a static bike or stand which allows you to ride a road bike but you go nowhere!

All of the above named activities, if engaged in reasonably often (2-4 times per week for many months), for a reasonable length of time (20-30 minutes), at a reasonable intensity (level 2 on the Effort Sense Rating scale) improve aerobic capacity (proficiency of heart and lungs). Also, they are low cost and require very little organisation. Some important advice on how to proceed follows. Please consider this carefully.

That entry to these activities requires a steady, progressive approach in terms of both duration and intensity. The adage 'don't run before you can walk' applies very well in this context. For example, if the aim is to run continuously for 20 minutes at effort level 2, the progression is walk, brisk walking, walking interspaced with jogging, jogging interspaced with walking, jogging, jogging interspersed with running, running interspersed with jogging, gradual reduction in jog time/gradual build up of the run time. This progressive-stage principle can be adapted to the other stamina activities and applies to all individuals who have not exercised regularly at quite a high level in the last six weeks. This includes recovery from injury. The de-training effect (inactivity) is virtually a mirror image of the training effect (activity).

Also it is unwise to set down hard and fast rules for time taken to build up to 20 or more minutes of continuous exercise or to cover specific distances in stamina activities. Rate of progress and level of performances are controlled by individual differences centred on a person's own assessment of the effort involved. If a person can sustain a run or swim for 20 minutes at their own effort sense rating of somewhat hard (level 2) they will have attained a level of healthy fitness in the stamina component.

In order to keep things interesting it is perhaps best to ring the changes with the activities. However, individual capability or preference may mean that you just stick to the same activity. A combination is recommended.

As heart and lung efficiency is the foundation of many sports and everyday tasks, it is advised that approximately 60% of exercise time is invested in stamina-type activities once a reasonable foundation of basic strength and suppleness has been achieved. You can also help yourself a bit by walking, climbing stairs etc. at every opportunity.

COOL DOWN

Every exercise session should end with a cool-down period to return your body towards its resting state. This should consist of some 5-10 minutes of activity at a similar level to the warm-up. Never stop exercising suddenly, always ease down.

Assessing Progress

It is a good idea to keep a diary of your exercise. This should include type and amount of exercise, how you felt etc. Once started, this acts as a motivational device, it charts progress and keeps you going. Every now and then assess your fitness using Effort Sense Rating Scale as you did at the beginning of this chapter. This is another means of determining whether progress is being made. Finally, don't just follow your programme irrespective of events. You must want to do it, it has to be enjoyable and will require persistence and effort to be of benefit. However, it is essential to 'listen' to the signals from your body they will tell you when to go and when to stop.

Enjoy your exercise by fitting it into your lifestyle. Keep it in perspective: don't let it rule your life. Participation at the right level is good for you and will make you feel good.

If you have been ill, suffer from a particular medical condition or are pregnant then **remember to consult your GP before beginning an exercise programme.**

MARIAN: *LIFEGUIDE* MEMBER

Marian is 45. She is a housewife. Marian joined Lifeguide because she felt she was in a rut. She was bored and felt that she needed more stimulation in her life but, like many people, found it difficult to give herself that extra push.

Marian found that through talking to the other women in the group about her problems and benefiting from the mutual support within the group, she became more confident and so better able to take positive steps to make her life more interesting. Whether it was the positive decision to get some help and support by joining the group initially, or by absorbing the tremendous warmth and energy produced by this group of women she doesn't exactly know: it was probably a combination of the two. Above all, confidence can be regained by realising that you are capable of making some of the decisions about your life.

Since joining Lifeguide Marian has joined a writing class and has produced some well-received poetry and short stories. Marian says,'The extra confidence I've gained through Lifeguide has enabled me to become motivated and I am now going to writing classes. But this confidence has also enabled me to cope with some of my stories being rejected. Instead of giving up as I once would have done, I just try again and see the rejection as a positive learning experience.'

CHAPTER FOUR

WOMEN'S HEALTH

WOMEN'S HEALTH

CERVICAL CANCER

The majority of women in this country have never had a smear test. And yet cervical smear tests are simple, painless examinations which take a couple of minutes to perform. It is an important area, then, for us to cover and in this section we hope to reassure you and hopefully to inspire you to be tested regularly. One of the main reasons for women not getting smear tests regularly is fear. Fear of the test itself and fear of the results. The fact is we owe it to ourselves to make sure that we are healthy.

When I was suddenly in the position recently of having to have treatment for pre-cancerous cells which had been found after my last cervical smear test, I realised that I was very ignorant of the facts. This ignorance bred fear and I went through a period of unnecessary anxiety about what was happening in my body - and all because I didn't have the right information to hand. Don't let this happen to you too. Read the facts and the information provided here and take any necessary steps to help yourself. Above all, don't avoid being tested - cervical cancer is not something that will go away if you forget about it.

THE FACTS:

NOTE:

Each year in Britain, 2000 women die from cervical cancer. These deaths are avoidable.

Cervical cancer is the only malignant cancer which is identifiable by a very simple test and which can be cured if treated early enough. 90% of those women who die from cervical cancer have never had a smear test. Cervical cancer becomes fatal when left untreated. Several million women in Britain have never had a smear test. There appear to be two main reasons why these women do not go for a smear test. They either avoid the test because they think it will take too much time and will be very painful; or they shut out the thoughts of cervical cancer from their minds completely - a sort of ostrich approach to cervical cancer!

NOTE: * **a smear test takes only a minute to perform, and although some women may find it uncomfortable (most don't suffer any discomfort at all), there is no pain involved at all.**

* **if you ignore the idea of cervical cancer and therefore never have a smear test, you stand more of a chance of dying from cervical cancer.**

The Cervical Smear Test can detect changes that can occur on the cervix. These changes are not cancerous, but pre-cancerous. If these changed cells are not treated they may become cancerous at a later stage.

WHAT IS THE CERVIX?

The cervix is the neck of the womb (see diagram). The narrow end of the womb which juts down into the vagina is the cervix. Those women who use a cap or coil for contraceptive purposes will have been taught how to find their cervix.

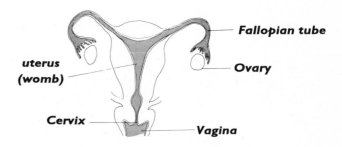

WHAT IS THE CERVICAL SMEAR TEST?

Devised by a Greek-American doctor George
Papanicolaou 60 years ago, the test consists of taking a
scraping of mucus and cells from a specific area in the
cervix.

The mucus contains tissue cells which have worked their
way to the surface of the cervix. This mucus is smeared
(hence the term 'smear test') onto a glass slide which is
then sent to a laboratory for analysis. In the laboratory,
the mucus is examined under a microscope in order to
detect abnormal cells, if any.

**NOTE: Abnormal cells warn of the possible development of
future cancer. They are not cancerous in themselves.**

At the laboratory, if the cells are found to be normal,
this is referred to as a negative result. If the cells are
found to be abnormal, this is a positive or abnormal
result and you should be referred back to the doctor or
clinic where you had the test done.

**NOTE: You should always make sure you find out the results
of your cervical smear test. Don't assume if you've
heard nothing, everything's all right. Ask at the place
where the test was carried out.**

A NEGATIVE RESULT

Remember, NEGATIVE = NORMAL

The majority of smear tests have a negative result. In
other words, at the time the test was carried, the cervix
was healthy. This does not mean that you never have to
have another smear test.

It is recommended that you should have smear tests at regular 3-5 yearly intervals. Never leave it more than 5 years.

AN ABNORMAL OR POSITIVE RESULT

If you have any of the following symptoms in between your smear tests, you must contact your doctor as soon as possible:

A positive result means that the cells collected from the cervix during the smear test were not normal. Changes in the cervix usually take place over a long period of time. Because of this the degree of change will vary from woman to woman.

- *Unusual discharge*

- *Bleeding after the menopause*

- *Discomfort*

- *Bleeding after intercourse*

- *Bleeding between periods*

Any change at all, minor or major, needs further investigation. Most changes are minor and often need only more frequent smear tests to monitor the situation.

More major changes will require investigation by a gynaecologist so as to see how far the changes have developed and to offer appropriate treatment where necessary.

NOTE

It is rare for a positive smear test to indicate that a cancer has already developed

REPEAT CERVICAL SMEAR TESTS

Sometimes you may be asked back for a repeat smear test - this is not always due to a positive result. You may be asked back for any of the following reasons:

1. The initial sample contained too few cells for an accurate reading

2. There may be an infection present which prevents an accurate reading - e.g., thrush.

3. The test may have been carried out just before a period and as such the sample will have been too difficult to examine.

WHAT IF MY SMEAR TEST RESULTS ARE POSITIVE?

Above all, don't panic. It is good that the abnormalities are detected now when they can be treated.

NOTE

The best time to have a smear test is half-way between periods

You will be referred to an out-patient clinic for investigation. The most common type of investigation is a colposcopy. The colposcope is a special microscope which enables the doctor to make a detailed examination of the cervix. During this examination, the doctor will take samples from the cervix. These very small samples are called **biopsies**. These samples will give a confirmation of the degree of change and will help the doctor to decide which form of treatment is appropriate.

DOES A COLPOSCOPY HURT?

A colposcopy involves no pain at all. No part of the colposcope will touch you and it is no different from having a smear test performed. The whole examination will take about 15 minutes. You will have a repeat smear and two solutions applied to your cervix.

TREATMENTS

LASER TREATMENT

NOTE

Laser treatment can be performed in an out-patients' clinic.

This is the most widely used form of treatment for abnormal cells on the cervix. The treatment involves a laser beam (intense light) which destroys the cells. Once the cells have been destroyed, the cervix will take a few weeks to heal properly. You will then be required to take follow-up smear tests at more frequent intervals than you are used to. You must go for your follow-up smear tests because you know that if you are being so closely monitored, you are in little danger of the cancer developing at a later date.

CONE BIOPSY

This form of treatment may be used as an alternative to laser treatment. It involves an operation to remove a cone-shaped piece from the centre of the cervix. If this is the treatment your gynaecologist recommends, you will need to be admitted to hospital for a few days as you would need a general anaesthetic.

NOTE

It is very unusual for any further treatment to be needed after a cone biopsy

The piece which is removed from your cervix is examined to make sure that it contains all the abnormal cells. If this is so, the taking of the biopsy has also been the treatment. As with the laser treatment, you would be required to have frequent follow-up smear tests after a cone biopsy.

HYSTERECTOMY

In some cases a hysterectomy may be needed. This is given careful consideration by the doctor treating you, however, and the decision is made based on facts about your age and whether or not you've had children.

When you have a hysterectomy the cervix, the uterus, and sometimes the ovaries, are removed. This may be advised if the cone biopsy has not removed all the abnormal cells or if the gynaecologist believes that this is the best treatment for a particular case.

This form of treatment is recommended only occasionally and particularly if you have associated problems with your periods. This operation would require a longer stay in hospital and a longer period of convalescence.

POINTS TO REMEMBER

- The smear test is designed to detect pre-cancerous cells

- The majority of patients are cured permanently by the first treatment given

- If you don't take a smear test now, you will have less chance of preventing cancer of the cervix later

- There is no pain involved at all

- It is a fast and simple test to take

It is estimated that up to 6 in every 10 women ignore invitations to take a cervical smear test. Why, when the test itself and the treatment is so simple and effective, do so many women run the risk of developing cervical cancer? It is clear from studies carried out that there is a severe lack of knowledge about cervical smear tests and the prevention of cervical cancer - this ignorance can prevent a woman from seeking the correct advice and treatment. The message is clear - have a smear test now if you haven't been examined in the last 3-5 years.

Some women are put off by the thought of having a smear test performed by their male doctor. If this idea bothers you and is preventing you from being examined, ask at your local surgery whether there is a female doctor or qualified nurse on the premises who can carry out the test. If there isn't, visit your local Family Planning Clinic where you can ask to be be treated by female staff.

If you are baffled by the medical jargon ask the doctor or nurse to explain what is happening to you. Don't feel

NOTE

*Don't be afraid
to ask questions!*

embarrassed because you think you ought to know more about your body. The only way to find out, after all, is to ask! They are more than happy to give you full explanations of what's going on - at my local Family Planning Clinic, a wonderful female doctor explained everything so clearly and simply to me, even drawing me a diagram! Doctors are not mind-readers - if you don't ask, they will assume you already understand the system.

ARE SOME PEOPLE MORE PRONE TO DEVELOPING CERVICAL CANCER THAN OTHERS?

MYTH

*Only women who
have had several
sexual partners are
at risk*

There is a link between sexual intercourse and the risk of developing changes on the cervix, so those women who have never had sexual intercourse are not at as much risk as sexually active women. This is untrue - even if you have only ever had one sexual partner, there is a chance you may develop changes on the cervix.

FACTS:

- Cervical cancer is rare in women who have never had sexual intercourse

- Cervical cancer is more common in women who began sexual activity during adolescence

- Cervical cancer is more common in women who smoke

- There may be a higher incidence of cervical disease if other women in your family have suffered from this also.

- Cervical cancer kills 2000 women every year in britain

*So don't delay -
have the test and
stay healthy!*

Comedienne Faith Brown is now a member of several charities which help women with cervical cancer. She has been through the cone biopsy treatment and is keen to tell other women what a life-saver the treatment actually is.

FAITH BROWN'S STORY ON CERVICAL CANCER

Finding out that I had abnormal precancerous cells in my cervix came as a complete shock to me. For a long time - since my daughter, Danielle, was born 12 years ago - I have had a medical check up every year. She is so important to me and I want to make sure that I am in perfect health for her sake as well as my own.

Well, I was feeling wonderful and people told me I looked well too - so imagine the shock when the clinic where I'd had my last smear test telephoned me and asked me to go back for a repeat test. I was devastated to learn that I had abnormal cells and that I had to go back to the clinic. But that was all I was told at that stage. The clinic told me to contact my doctor and things would be taken from there. I had only been with my doctor for about a year then and didn't know him very well, but I telephoned him and told him what the clinic had said. I was by this time feeling very anxious and very frightened - the first thought that went through my head was 'What's going to happen to my husband and to Danielle if something awful happens to me?' I was petrified and imagining all sorts of horrific things. So I telephoned my doctor, expecting reassurance and information. I didn't get it. He was, in fact, even quite dismissive of my worries and he made me feel worse than I had done before I phoned him. My husband was furious and insisted I rang the clinic immediately. I went to see them the next day and they were wonderful. They explained what everything meant and that I would have to have a cone biopsy. Again I panicked. And again I was reassured. I began to realise that as long as I was being seen to and being treated, I was going to be OK. They had caught my cells before they became cancerous and, with this simple operation, they were going to be able to cure it.

I went in for the operation which was performed under general anaesthetic. I felt no pain or discomfort afterwards - which astonished me - and in fact I found it a far less disturbing experience than going to the dentist! Some time afterwards, I was being interviewed by a female journalist on the telephone. We were chatting and she told me that she was very worried about her sister who had had a positive smear test result. So I told her that I'd had a cone biopsy and that she should tell her sister that there's really nothing to worry about. The fact that she was being treated was a positive thing, not something to worry about. And then the journalist asked me to consider making some sort of statement about my experiences because she thought it might help other women. And I thought, well why not? I did feel very strongly about the issue, after all. After I had done several interviews about my experiences, I began to get lots of positive feedback from people. One day, a 24 year old woman stopped me in the street and said that because of reading about my experience, she'd been prompted to go and have a smear test, even though she looked and felt very well. It turned out she did have to have treatment for precancerous cells - but if she had never read the article, she said, she would never have thought about going to be tested and her abnormal cells would have gone undetected and may have developed into cervical cancer.

So you can see the importance of having regular cervical smear tests. If you have abnormal cells, it won't show in your appearance and you won't necessarily show any physical symptoms. If you do have any abnormalities, as long as they're detected early enough, you can be successfully treated. Just remember that treatment is positive - ignoring it is not.

And a final word - I get many letters from women who seem to believe that cervical cancer is associated with promiscuity. Well let me tell you, hand on my heart, that I have only ever had one boyfriend in my whole life - and I married him! So don't assume that because you've only had one partner you are immune because you're not.

Be tested regularly and keep your peace of mind - after all, we only have one body and it should last a lifetime. You owe it to yourself to look after yourself. So don't be scared and don't hide your head in the sand - go and be tested now. It's definitely worth it!

BREAST CANCER

When was the last time that you examined your breasts for lumps? Do you even know how to do it? In this section of the book, we aim to not only explain the phenomenon of breast cancer but we will also include diagrams and instructions on how to carry out a self-examination.

SO WHAT IS BREAST CANCER?

IMPORTANT

Not all tumours are cancerous!

Breasts are made up of glands and fatty tissue. These glands and fatty tissue are made up of cells. The cells can divide to form lumps. These lumps are known as tumours. If the tumour is cancerous or malignant, it can spread. Without treatment, the tumour will destroy the surrounding tissue and secondary tumours may develop.

SYMPTOMS

- **any unusual lump in the breast**
- **dark discharge from the nipple**
- **indentation of the nipple**

In most cases, these symptoms are not accompanied by any pain.

TREATMENT

Recent studies have shown that a radical mastectomy (removal of the breast) is not necessarily the best form of treatment. Increasingly, surgeons prefer to perform a **lumpectomy**- this means rather than removing the whole of the breast, simply removing the lump itself, plus any surrounding tissue. This form of surgery is followed up with radiotherapy, chemotherapy and/or medication to contain and eradicate any stray cells.

ARE SOME PEOPLE MORE SUSCEPTIBLE TO BREAST CANCER THAN OTHERS?

Although all the causes of breast cancer are not fully understood, certain groups of women have been identified as more likely to develop breast cancer than others. For instance:

- **if any close female relatives have suffered from this disease**
- **women who have had no children or who have had them late in life**

Don't panic - just because you fit into one of these categories, it does not automatically mean that you will develop cancer of the breast. But it does mean that you should monitor any changes in your breasts very carefully.

NOTE

Only I in 10 lumps that grow in a woman's breast is cancerous

Some people have linked the contraceptive pill with the development of breast cancer - the link is very tenuous indeed. Studies show that in the 30 years since the introduction of the pill, the incidence of breast cancer has not increased significantly in either the UK or the United States. It must be noted also that the pill has positive effects in that it lowers the incidence of cancer of the ovary and uterus.

WHAT CAN I DO TO HELP MYSELF?

It is vital that all women, including those who are not in the high-risk groups, learn to perform a self-examination. This examination should be done every month, so as to note any changes which may have occurred. Please remember that some women's breasts are naturally more lumpy than others. This doesn't mean you have a cancerous lump. If you are worried, however, go to your GP or your Family Planning Clinic immediately.

Now study the diagrams and examine your breasts. The best time to do your self-examination is just after your period has finished. Make a note of the day you perform the self-examination, so that you can repeat the exercise at the same time each month. If it helps to reassure you, keep a sort of diary detailing what you felt.

Above all, remember that you should get to know your own body and its idiosyncracies. Don't panic if you think you've found a lump - it will usually turn out to be nothing at all! If you do find a lump, go immediately to your GP or local clinic. You are asking for problems if you neglect your worries.

SELF-EXAMINATION

1.Stand in front of a mirror with your back straight and your arms by your side. Look at your breasts. Now ask yourself these questions:

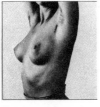

1

- has there been any change in the size?
- has one become lower than the other?
- has one nipple begun to turn inwards?
- do you have any discharge from either nipple?
- is the skin puckering, dimpling or is the texture changed?

2.Now raise your hands above your head and look at the part of the breast leading to the armpit.

2

- is there any swelling?
- is the skin puckering? Lower your arms and raise them again. Repeat this action, all the while watching your nipples.
- do they move the same distance?

3

3. Now look down at your breasts and squeeze each nipple gently; check for any bleeding or discharge that is unusual for you.

4. Now lie down in a relaxed position and make yourself comfortable with your head on a pillow. Examine one breast at a time. Put a folded towel under your shoulder-blade in the side you are examining. This helps to spread the breast tissue and make examination easier.

4

5. Place your left arm under your head. With the flat of your right hand, keeping your fingers straight and close together, slide your hand over your left breast. Start at the armpit and work around the breast moving your hand in an anti-clockwise circular direction, gradually moving inwards towards the nipple. Make sure that you have felt all parts of the breast.

5

6. Now bring your left arm down to your side and, again with your right hand, feel for lumps in your armpit. Start right up in the hollow of your armpit and gradually work your way down towards your breast. It is important not to forget this last part of the examination

6

7. Now repeat the whole exercise on your right breast.

REMEMBER

Only 1 in every 10 lumps found in the breast is cancerous

If you detect anything which worries you, or notice any change from month to month, you must consult your doctor. If you are embarrassed about seeing your own male doctor, visit a **Family Planning Clinic** where you can ask to be seen by a female doctor.

THE MENOPAUSE

Menopause means the end of your menstruating phase. It means that when menopause has occurred, no more eggs are released in your body and you can therefore no longer have children.

The onset of the menopause can mean different things to different women. For instance, two out of every ten women report that they have no problems at all with the menopause, whereas others report that not only do they suffer physical symptoms, but emotional ones too.

The menopause can be a very difficult time for many women and so it is important that you understand what is happening to your body and that you have the understanding and support of those around you.

PHYSICAL EFFECTS

You may notice signs of the menopause three or four years before your last ever period - in some cases, though, it can be for ten years before the last period. This is the period in which your body is adjusting to the hormonal changes taking place. Once your periods have stopped, it may take a further year or two for your body to settle down into its new state. Rest assured, though, the symptoms will eventually stop.

HOT FLUSHES OR THE SWEATS

Hot flushes are caused by tiny blood vessels in the skin opening up suddenly and filling quickly with blood. This causes the skin to become hot and red for anything from 15 seconds to one minute. Gradually the skin calms down again. Hot flushes can happen any time with unregulated frequency throughout the day and night and vary in strength from woman to woman. Although these flushes are annoying, they are not harmful. But it can be very distressing to wake up in the middle of the night feeling faint, hot and drenched with sweat. You may feel slightly dizzy during a hot flush; this mechanism is not entirely understood but may be caused by a sudden rush of blood to the skin which can momentarily cut down the amount of oxygen reaching the brain. The heart may also beat faster to cope with the change in blood flow, which accounts for the palpitations you may feel.

WHY DO MY PERIODS STOP?

Each month, a woman's body prepares itself for pregnancy. This is done by internal hormone production. The two hormones are **oestrogen** and **progesterone. Oestrogen** is produced by the ovaries, after which it is carried in the blood to the uterus (to build up the lining of the uterus) and to the vagina to increase lubrication. Once an egg has been released from the ovary, the other hormone, **progesteron**e, completes the preparation of the uterus. If no pregnancy occurs, the level of both hormones drops. The bleeding you experience during your period is the lining of the uterus coming away to make room for the next period of hormonal activity.

The reason that your periods stop is that as a woman gets older her ovaries produce less and less oestrogen. As such the monthly menstrual cycle is disrupted and eventually the periods stop.

If you start to notice changes in your monthly cycle, you should keep a note of the frequency of your periods, the

For most women, hot flushes, sweating and palpitations are not severe. There are some practical tips which can help to cut down the effects of these changes within your body:

- *as stress can make these symptoms far worse than they need be, try and learn some relaxation techniques*

- *if you are taking any medication, ask your doctor whether this could be making the symptoms worse*

- *to help with sweating at night, always use cotton sheets and wear cotton night-clothes. Nylon will make the situation worse.*

- *avoid spicy foods, alcohol, and caffeine as these make the flushes worse. Avoid them particularly from the early evening onwards.*

heaviness or lightness of the periods from month to month and how long it lasts. In this way you can monitor your progress towards menopause, and it will help your doctor to decide whether your bleeding is normal.

MENOPAUSE AND THE FEAR OF PREGNANCY

This is a common worry amongst women nearing the menopause. Because there are long gaps between periods, it is easy to think it could be due to pregnancy. If you feel worried about this, contact your doctor or your Family Planning Clinic immediately.

Most doctors advise that a woman over 50 should wait until their periods have been stopped for over a year before stopping contraception. If women are under 50, they are advised to continue using contraception for two years, to be on the safe side.

IS THERE SEX AFTER MENOPAUSE?

The answer to this question is emphatically yes! There is no reason why sex should stop after menopause. Because of the changes in your body, however, there are sometimes problems which need dealing with in order for your sexual activity to continue undeterred. One such problem which many women suffer from is vaginal dryness.

Vaginal dryness can be a very embarrassing subject to bring up with your doctor - but if you have this problem and you don't deal with it, your sex life will probably grind to an unnecessary halt! Remember that the oestrogen produced in your body helps to lubricate the vagina. So when the level of oestrogen drops as you get older, vaginal lubrication is lessened, and so vaginal dryness becomes a problem. A simple answer to this problem is to use a lubricating jelly. This is available over the counter in any chemist shop. This will work for most people.

However, if the vagina continues to be dry and sore, during intercourse, your doctor can provide more help. If you are too embarrassed to talk with your male doctor, visit a clinic where you can ask to see a female doctor, such as your local **Family Planning Clinic**. But do remember, even if your doctor is male, he is there to help you and he will be sympathetic. Pluck up your courage and trust him. A doctor can prescribe a course of oestrogen cream, or in more serious cases, a course of hormone replacement tablets.

Vaginal dryness is an important problem and one you must sort out, not only for the sake of your sex life. The natural lubrication of the vagina helps to prevent infection. So obviously if that natural lubrication facility disappears, you are more likely to suffer from infection.

Many women fear that they will lose interest in sex after menopause. This is not always the case. In fact, because the fear of unwanted pregnancy has vanished, many women find that their sexual appetite increases!

And don't feel that sex is just for the youngsters! Although sexual interest lessens to some extent with age for both men and women, lots of people enjoy a fulfilling sex life well into their 70s and 80s!

- *if you are on any medication, ask your doctor whether this could be having any side-effects*

- *discuss your difficulties with your partner. If you leave things unsaid, there is a possibility you will grow apart and this will cause more problems*

- *seek help with a counsellor. Someone from Relate can help you with any relationship problems, be they physical or emotional*

- *try and reduce any stress in your life - interest in sex often returns naturally when you are relaxed and content.*

If you find that your appetite for sex is less, or even non-existent, after menopause and that there is no apparent physical reason for this (such as vaginal dryness), check the following:

MENOPAUSAL MYTHS!

Everyone has some advice to offer a woman approaching menopause, based on their experience with a mother or a sister or a friend. But remember that every woman is different and as such experiences different menopausal symptoms. Here are some examples of myths surrounding menopause;

'I started my periods when I was 11, so I'm bound to have an early menopause'

This is not true. No link has been found between the age you started your periods at and the age at which you experience menopause.

'Well, my mother didn't go through menopause until she was well into her 50s, so I've got a long time to go yet!'

This is not a foregone conclusion. Menopausal symptoms can be affected by lifestyle, living conditions and stress. Obviously these things vary a lot between mother and daughter and therefore their menopausal experiences can be quite different too.

'I suffer terribly from pre-menstrual tension, so I'm dreading the menopause!'

Just because you may have had trouble with PMT, don't automatically assume you will have difficulties during menopause. There is no direct link between the two. One of the wonderful things that happens after menopause is that pre-menstrual tension disappears completely.

MENOPAUSE AND OSTEOPOROSIS

Osteoporosis is a medical condition linked with menopause. It is a disease in which the bones become lighter and more brittle as the calcium is lost from them. For older people, this can mean a gradual shrinking in height, a bending of the spine and a tendency for bones to break more easily than ever before.

Men and women begin to lose the calcium from their bones from the age of about 35 onwards. After menopause, some women lose the calcium at an increased rate. Again, this is because of the dramatic drop in oestrogen levels before and during menopause. The effect of an increased loss of calcium may not be evident until the woman is in her 70s, when brittle bones become noticeable. This does not, however, happen to every woman. Some naturally retain a relatively high level of oestrogen after menopause which prevents such a rapid loss of calcium.

REMEMBER

Calcium in milk products is absorbed more efficiently than in other types of food.

So in this case, prevention is the best cure. You can help to prevent the onset of osteoporosis by modifying your diet. To keep healthy bones and cut down the risk of osteoporosis, eat lots of foods which are rich in calcium, and get plenty of exercise. (With any exercise undertaken, particularly if you have a medical condition, you must consult your GP first.)

As a general rule, women need between 500 and 1,000 mg of calcium daily in order to stay healthy and to help prevent brittle bones in later life. One pint (0.56 litres) of milk and one 5 oz (141.5g) carton of yoghurt together contain about 1,000 of calcium.

Getting your daily requirement of calcium is made easier these days because most packaging lists the nutritional contents of the food. (See the Chapter on Diet for further information on calcium rich food). If you're worried about the fat content of milk, simply choose a low fat type.

Get plenty of fresh air - half an hour outdoors every day can do you no end of good!

HORMONE REPLACEMENT THERAPY AND MENOPAUSE

You have probably heard much in the media about this new treatment, often referred to as HRT. But what is it exactly? And how can it help you? This form of treatment is designed to give you extra oestrogen to replace that which you are losing naturally when you approach menopause. Remember the drop in oestrogen levels causes vaginal dryness and eventually causes your periods to stop. By taking in this extra oestrogen, your hormone levels will regain a constancy they have lost naturally and you will suffer less from hot flushes and your vagina will remain lubricated. HRT also prevents heart disease and strokes.

HRT is usually taken in the form of low dosage pills, and sometimes in the form of self-adhesive skin patches, A course of treatment can last from between 6 months to several years. The dosage is then gradually reduced when the body is capable of dealing with its new post-menopausal state.

HRT helps prevent osteoporosis or brittle bones. As it maintains a functional level of oestrogen, so it prevents the rapid loss of calcium which causes osteoporosis.

NOTE

THE RISKS OF HRT

Not everyone can
take HRT
For those women
suffering from the
following medical
conditions HRT
should not usually
be prescribed:

• possible cancer of
the breast or uterus
• liver/gall-bladder
disease
• undiagnosed
bleeding from the
vagina
• fibroid problems
• varicose veins
• those with close
relatives who have
suffered from
cancer of the
breast or uterus

Current views on the benefits and disadvantages of
hormone replacement therapy are strong and emotive.
Those women who have been helped through
menopause with this treatment see it as a life-saver. But
there are disadvantages to this treatment as well. There
is a slightly greater risk of gall-bladder disease and an
increased risk of cancer of the uterus if progestogen (the
other reproductive hormone) is not added to the
treatment.

There may be a slightly increased risk of breast cancer
after long term use but mainly doctors feel that the
benefits of preventing osteoporosis, heart disease and
stroke probably outweigh the potential risks.

Women who have long since ceased to have periods
start to experience monthly bleeding when having HRT.
Some women are not able to tolerate HRT well and may
decide to stop taking it. Discuss the subject of hormone
replacement therapy with your doctor. Ask him or her
to explain to you fully the pros and cons of such a
treatment and then decide together whether it's a
suitable treatment for you or whether there is an
alternative.

**Remember that the long term risks of hormone
replacement therapy are not yet known.**

MENOPAUSE AND MOODS

The menopause has, in some ignorant circles, because
synonymous with madness, and because of this myth
many women actually believe that they are going to lose

- *frequent periods of crying*
- *forgetfulness*
- *insomnia*
- *poor appetite*
- *lethargy*
- *loss of sexual appetite*
- *palpitations*
- *excessive worrying about small things*
- *feeling worthless and a failure*
- *lack of concentration*
- *indecisiveness*
- *irritability*

control of their faculties during menopause. This is not true!

What can happen, however, is that your moods may change more quickly due to the disruption in your hormone levels during menopause. Many women say they feel depressed, irritable and tired during menopause. But before you start blaming every emotion and unreasonable feeling on the menopause, stop!

There are other factors which could be making you feel the way you do, admittedly not helped by the changes happening in your body, but not necessarily caused by them. Sit down and list the possible problem areas in your life. It could be work, family, your marriage, money or any number of different problems. The best thing is to work out the real reason for your feelings of depression or irritability. Don't hide behind the menopause - rather accept that it may make you more susceptible to these feelings, but look for the real cause of the problem first.

LIFEGUIDE GROUPS

TRICIA: *LIFEGUIDE* MEMBER

Tricia is a very bright and bubbly 45 year old. She is an ex-nursery nurse, and now works as a personal assistant in a small business.

Tricia came to Lifeguide because she wanted to feel more confident about herself. She had two main goals - the first was to learn to say no to people, and the second was to fultil her ambition of thirty years, to write children's stories.

Her first goal may seem odd at first glance - surely everyone can say no if they want to? Well you can't if you feel worried that people won't like you or love you if you refuse their demands. This problem has cropped up again and again since we began Lifeguide. Many people feel that if they do not always fulfil other people's expectations of them and respond to their demands, then those people will stop loving them. Tricia felt that saying no to other people was a problem for her. Lifeguide and the discussion groups have helped her to become more confident about herself. Being more confident has enabled Tricia to know that she can say no to other people without them rejecting her. And now when she does give her time and attention to others, it is because she wants to, not because it's what she thinks is expected of her.

Tricia has also decided to make her dream of writing children's stories come true. She has now gained the confidence and support to not only write the stories, but to send them off to publishers too. She says: 'I know there's a possibility that they may be rejected. But I also know that I can deal with that now if it happens. I'll just try again. The important thing to me is that I've done it - I've written the stories, and I feel proud of myself.'

SMOKING~A SYMPATHETIC GUIDE TO STOPPING

CHAPTER FIVE

SMOKING ~
A SYMPATHETIC GUIDE TO STOPPING

Hang on - don't turn the page! This isn't going to be yet another glib piece of prose on the virtues of stopping smoking. I promise - no moralising. I have been a heavy smoker for half my life so far and I know that there is nothing worse than a smug ex-smoker or non-smoker eulogising about the virtues of not smoking.

But...the fact is that if we continue to smoke, there is every chance that we will die prematurely of some horrible smoking-related disease.

It's easy in your teenage years and early20s to feel as though you're immortal. Everyone else gets cancer, but not me! I'm young, fit and healthy! People become aware of their own mortality at different stages in their lives - with me it was my 30th birthday. Since I started smoking when I was 15, I had always perceived myself as just a 'young smoker' - that is, I wouldn't still be smoking in middle age or anything like that. And yet there I was, nearly 30, and still smoking more than ever. (I hate to admit it, but I have smoked 40 a day for the last five years at least). On top of this realisation, I discovered at the same time that I had to have treatment for pre-cancerous cells to prevent the development of cervical cancer (see Chapter on **Women's Health**). My doctor told me that my smoking was probably partly to blame for this. I was scared stiff and I made the decision to stop smoking. I don't want to die young, as my grandmother did at 64, of lung cancer or other smoking-related diseases - and I don't think anyone else should either.

SMOKING : THE FACTS

~ **110,000 people die because of smoking in Great Britain every year.**

If you smoke cigarettes, you are more likely to suffer from the following diseases and medical conditions than someone who has never smoked:

- *Coronary heart disease*
- *Lung cancer*
- *Chronic Bronchitis*
- *Emphysema*
- *Congestive cardiac failure*
- *Respiratory diseases*
- *Cancer of the mouth*
- *Cancer of the pharynx*
- *Cancer of the larynx*
- *Cancer of the pancreas*
- *Cancer of the bladder*
- *Peptic ulceration*
- *Asthma*
- *Hypertension*

~ One in six of all premature deaths is caused by smoking.

~ 33% (or 15 million) of adults in England and Wales smoke.

~ 25% of adolescents have begun to smoke by the time they leave school.

~ On average, if you smoke 20 cigarettes a day, you will shorten your life by 10-15 years.

~ If you smoke during pregnancy, your baby will weigh on average half a pound (225 g)less than babies born to women who do not smoke.

~ 40% of smokers die before retirement age.

~ Tobacco causes 90% of lung cancer deaths, 80% of bronchitis deaths, 30% of all cancer deaths, and 30% of all deaths from heart disease and strokes.

WHAT IS IN CIGARETTES TO MAKE THEM SO HARMFUL?

1.NICOTINE

Nicotine is the element within cigarettes which is addictive. If you smoke, you are a nicotine addict. Smoking cigarettes is an extremely effective way of getting nicotine into your brain. As you take each little puff on your cigarette, you put nicotine into your brain and stimulate the nervous system. The deeper the inhalation of smoke, the greater the effect of the nicotine. It is extremely pleasurable and acts as a relaxant or tranquiliser. In stressful situations you tend to inhale more deeply than usual on your cigarette. You also tend to hold the smoke longer in your lungs before exhaling. High levels of nicotine in your blood produce a relaxing effect. The deeper the drag, the more relaxed you become. In studies carried out on the addictive powers of nicotine, it has been found that when the nicotine level in your blood drops below a certain level, you feel a renewed desire to smoke to replenish that nicotine level. When cigarettes are treated to remove some of the nicotine, the smoker will simply increase the number of cigarettes smoked, thereby retaining a high intake of nicotine. Similarly, if the cigarette is treated to increase the level of nicotine in each one, the smoker will smoke fewer cigarettes.

NICOTINE REPLACEMENT THERAPY Many people find this a great help when stopping smoking and the most common and widely available form of treatment is nicotine chewing gum. This gum releases nicotine slowly into the blood stream, and studies show that smokers who use this form of treatment are twice as likely to be successful at stopping smoking and staying stopped than those who don't use it. At the time of writing, nicotine gum is only available on prescription from your GP, but plans are underway to make it available over the counter at chemists by the end of 1991. Nicotine gum is quite safe to use: it does not cause cancer or any other disease. The nicotine intake from one piece of gum is equal to one third of the nicotine intake from a cigarette, and without all the harmful and dangerous tars, chemicals and carbon monoxide. By using the gum, you will slowly cure your addiction. The gum should be used for a minimum of three months and then its use should be gradually reduced and stopped.

2. CARBON MONOXIDE (CO)
Carbon monoxide is a colourless, odourless, poisonous gas produced by burning organic material. It mainly affects the heart, blood vessels and lungs. When tobacco

smoke is inhaled into the lungs, carbon monoxide passes through the lining of the lung into the bloodstream where it becomes attached to haemoglobin (found in red blood cells). Red blood cells carry oxygen around the body. But they have a much higher chemical attraction to carbon monoxide than to oxygen (200 times greater), so if there is any carbon monoxide in the blood at all it becomes attached to haemoglobin in place of the oxygen. This forms carboxyhaemoglobin, or COHb. So the percentage of COHb is the proportion of red blood cells which are carrying carbon monoxide instead of oxygen. If you have, therefore, 5% of COHb, your body is 5% short of oxygen. Oxygen deficiency means that your system is under greater strain than normal. The heart has to work harder to compensate for the oxygen loss. Studies show that heavy smokers have a COHb average level of 8%, which means that they are 8% short of oxygen.

3. TAR
Cigarette tar is the name given to the group of chemicals which are generally accepted as being a potential cause of cancer. It is thought that hydrocarbons contained in tar interact to initiate, promote and accelerate cancer. These hydrocarbons, along with other substances contained in tobacco tar, act as irritants to the lung and may be implicated in causing or aggravating bronchitis and other respiratory diseases.

REASONS FOR STOPPING SMOKING

1. YOUR HEALTH
Let's assume that you want to live as long as possible. If you smoke cigarettes, you are likely to reduce the length of your life. Read again the list of smoking-related diseases. I know if you're a fit and healthy 25 or even 35

year old, it is difficult to imagine being disabled through a smoking-related disease. But if you don't stop now, you run a very high risk of not only ending your life unnecessarily early but also of living part of it as an invalid.

2. OTHERS' HEALTH: PASSIVE SMOKING - FACT OR FICTION?

We've all heard this argument many times from hardened and defensive smokers (you may have used this one yourself): 'It's my life - if I want to smoke, I will. It's my business!' But is it really just your business? Are we actually harming other people by smoking in their company? The short answer is: yes, we are.

When you smoke a cigarette, two types of smoke are produced: 'mainstream smoke' and 'sidestream smoke.' Mainstream is the smoke which you, as the smoker, inhale deliberately from your cigarette, which passes through the filter and into your body. Sidestream smoke is that which goes straight into the air which everyone breathes. This sidestream smoke remains unfiltered and therefore contains high concentrations of the harmful substances which make tobacco smoke dangerous.

Think about the consequences of sidestream smoke. If you are smoking in a public place, a restaurant, for instance, the non-smoker at the next table is forced to inhale the harmful substances which you choose to inhale yourself. So whilst it is your choice and your life, it is likely that you are damaging other people's health too. It has been proven that passive smokers can have a decreased lung function similar to that of light smokers of cigarettes. Recent studies also show that passive smoking may also increase the risk of lung cancer. It's a pretty depressing thought, isn't it? Even if you decide to protect your health and be a non-smoker, you are at risk from smoking-related diseases because of those around you who smoke. The dangers of passive smoking are usually the basis for the non-smoker's argument, and, as you will no doubt realise, it is a valid one.

How wonderful if would be if life were simple and us smokers could simply decide to never again smoke a cigarette - no hard feelings, I just won't have any more. Sorry about all the damage so far, it won't happen again!

But, as all those smokers out there know, life ain't that wonderful! The fact is we are all nicotine addicts. We are capable of stopping smoking, but it will be difficult. There are some lucky people around who seem to have been able to just give up at the drop of a hat (or a cigarette butt) - but they are few and far between.

3. MONEY!

There's no way out of this argument: the fact is you are probably spending between £5 and £20 a week on cigarettes. Just think about what you could do with all that cash. (I've noticed however hard up I am, I have always been able to find enough for a packet of fags...)

If you smoke 20 cigarettes a day, you spend over £12 a week. If you make this an annual cost, the figure is more than £600 a year. That's £1,200 a year saved for those who smoke 40 cigarettes a day! Just think what you could do with all that money...

Once you've totted up how much you spend each day on cigarettes, decide that you're going to put the same

SMOKING

Date/Day	Amount saved
Monday	£ 1.75
Tuesday	£ 1.75
Wednesday	£ 1.75
Thursday	£ 1.75
Friday	£ 1.75
Saturday	£ 1.75
Sunday	£ 1.75
Weekly total:	£12.25

amount of money away each day when you stop smoking. This way you will see the material benefit of stopping smoking and enjoy planning what you can do with the money you save. To help you with this, why not buy a little pocket exercise book which you can use as a savings record. Set each page out as shown on the left. You can see the figure significantly growing week by week, and it is a useful positive and immediate result of you stopping smoking. At the end of each month, you could even transfer the money into a savings account at your bank or building society.

4. ATTRACTIVENESS

How can you look attractive when your teeth and fingers are tinged with yellow, your clothes and hair are smelly and your breath is stale? When I was a little girl, my grandmother came to visit quite often. I distinctly remember the horrible smell of her when she came into a room. I conveniently forgot about this aspect of smoking when I began demolishing 20 a day in my teens. I suppose this is what non-smokers thought about me when I smoked.

5. SOCIALISING

Socialising is becoming more and more difficult for the determined smoker. Going out for dinner is a good example; many restaurants now divide their premises into smoking and non-smoking areas. Your spaghetti carbonara tends to lose its appeal when you're sitting next to the men's toilets all evening! Friends' houses have also become a danger zone for the heavy smoker. More and more people are declaring their homes a non-smoking area;the only alternative is to slip out into the garden for a quick fag, but this only leaves you feeling abandoned, resentful - and cold.

BE SYMPATHETIC TOWARDS SMOKERS

This section is aimed at all ex-smokers (often the worst anti-smokers!) and non-smokers. First of all, to the ex-smokers reading this chapter...

Congratulations that you have conquered your addiction to nicotine! But please don't be smug about it. Perhaps it was easy for you to stop smoking - if so, don't assume it will be as easy for everyone else because it won't. So spare a little sympathy for those around you who might need some support in stopping smoking.

Now, to those of you who are lucky enough never to have smoked...
OK, so it's a disgusting habit and we're all polluting the communal air. We're sorry! You must try and understand that it is not at all easy to stop smoking once you have become addicted to nicotine. When I was smoking heavily, I used to feel guilty about the effect I was having on non-smokers. But I felt bad if I didn't have a cigarette for any length of time. Short of stopping altogether, I made a tremendous effort when I was with non-smokers to fit in with them. And so I should when you consider the dangers of passive smoking. But I noticed that non-smokers are decidedly unsympathetic towards smokers. The effort was all on my part. I think all I wanted was for them to realise the predicament I was in. So, if you know someone who has an addiction to nicotine, be sympathetic. Be firm in your anti-smoking views, because they are correct, but understand the difficulties which lie ahead of the person who's stopping smoking, and be positive about what they're trying to do.

STOPPING SMOKING!

This is the section which can change your life. You can stop smoking. So read on...

Our expert on the subject of stopping smoking is a familiar face to regular ITV daytime viewers, as *This Morning's* resident GP, medical expert and author of *Chris Steele's Smokers' Quit Plan* . One of only four experts on stopping smoking in this country, I think Chris is one of the most sympathetic non-smokers I've ever met. Chris runs clinics in two hospitals in Manchester for stopping smoking, and he has had an amazing success rate; his secret lies in his approach to smokers. He doesn't moralise. He presents the facts, the pros (there aren't any) and the cons. He understands the terrible grip of the addiction and he offers sympathy and sound advice. He is with you in the struggle to stop smoking. The smoker who is trying to stop doesn't feel defensive when Chris counsels him and I felt inspired by his dedication and his enthusiasm. For those people who can't get to his clinics, *Chris' Smoker's Quit Plan* is the answer. The book contains useful tips, realistic advice and moral support for those who are determined to stop smoking.

Here are ten tips from Dr Chris Steele which together can help you to stop smoking:

1	*Name the day:*	*Decide on a specific day when you will stop smoking and commit yourself to that day.*
2	*Quit with a friend:*	*Like most problems, stopping smoking is easier when you do it with a friend, or even as part of a group. The mutual moral support will be vital.*

SMOKING

3	**Cash not ash**	Find a jar or container to put the money you would have spent on cigarette into and watch it mount up. Plan what you will treat yourself to at the end of each month - if you smoke 20 cigarettes a day, you'll have nearly £50 a month to play with!
4	**Shift all cigarettes**	Prepare to stop. Rid your house and car of cigarettes, dirty ashtrays and lighters. Don't keep a safety pack of ciggies anywhere.
5	**Just for today**	Take one day at a time. Don't panic about what life will be like without cigarettes. Tell yourself, 'I'm not giving up forever. I'm just not smoking today.' Feel proud of yourself after each day is completed successfully and smoke free.
6	**Distract yourself**	Distract your hands with play things (e.g. worry beads); your mouth with oral stimulation (such as chewing gum); and your brain with something you like doing (such as a hobby, reading or writing).
7	**Refusing cigarettes**	From the day you have stopped smoking, remember that when someone offers you a cigarette, don't say, 'No, I've given up.' Think of yourself as a non-smoker not an ex-smoker and say, 'No thanks, I don't smoke.' If the offer is from someone who knows you smoke, tell a white lie and simply say you've just had one. Remember, if a smoker thinks you have just given up, you will be vulnerable to pressure from them to join them in 'just one more'.
8	**Nicotine Replacement Therapy**	The only such treatment available at the moment is nicotine gum. This is the best way of stopping smoking. Forget cutting down. Forget switching to milder brands - it doesn't work (see section on nicotine for a fuller explanation). Remember, tobacco kills - nicotine doesn't.

9 Fat Farewell Diet

If you're worried about putting on weight when you stop smoking, then turn to the section where full details of this weight-loss programme are given. But remember - ignore the weight problem for the first two weeks of stopping smoking. You cannot concentrate on both at once. You will not become enorm- ous in two weeks. And if you can stop smoking, you can certainly lose weight. It is more dangerous to smoke than to be overweight.

10 If you don't succeed

Remember that you cannot 'have just one cigarette'. This could be your downfall. The likelihood is that if you have 'just one more', you will start smoking again. If you return to smoking, be philosophical about and try again. Look at why you started again and learn from your mistakes. If you don't succeed, it really isn't the end of the world - as long as you try again, avoiding the pitfalls from the last time.

REMEMBER

Your mistakes are positive earning experiences

One person who has given up with Chris' help and is a testimony to the success of the ten point plan is actor Dean Sullivan, who you might know better as Jimmy Corkhill from *Brookside*. Here's his story:

DEAN SULLIVAN'S STORY ABOUT SMOKING

Well, I started smoking when I was 17 and stopped forever in January 1990 when I was 35. I had tried before to stop, and every day when I had my first cigarette I used to think, 'I've really got to give up' - but I had never been successful before. Stopping this time is different from all the other times for two reasons. Firstly, I acknowledged to myself that I was a nicotine addict - realising this gave me the jolt I needed to do something positive about my addiction. Secondly, I made the decision to stop. Instead of putting it off and making vague plans to stop in the future, I named the day and made a commitment to myself to stop on that day.

Both of these reasons for stopping smoking were very positive: by coming to terms with the real problems of smoking and realising that I was a nicotine addict, I could then take positive steps to get help with stopping smoking. I think nicotine addiction is like any other; when you're an alcoholic, you don't suddenly stop being an alcoholic because you're not drinking. You can't have just one more drink because it will return you to your previous drinking habits. So I knew this time that one of the reasons I'd failed so many times before was that I'd thought I could have just one more cigarette. You can't do that. Once you've had just one more cigarette, before you know it you've been out and bought a whole packet. And before long you're smoking as normal again.

The other positive aspect of stopping was committing myself to stopping on a particular day. I have often thought, 'Oh yes, well, I will give up, but I'll just wait until I've been on my holidays,' or 'until after Christmas,' or 'until I've done this or that.' That doesn't work. You're just putting it off. You have to write down the day you are going to stop and stick to that commitment, asChris advises in his *Smokers' Quit Plan*.

The day before, I cleared the car and the house of all signs of cigarettes and smoking, but kept one cigarette to have as my last one before going to bed. The next morning was crucial. Just as Chris advises, I didn't start panicking because I could never have another cigarette ever again in my life. I just thought 'OK, I'm not going to smoke today.' So I chewed the nicotine gum, and it was

SMOKING

so much easier than I thought it was going to be. I had no cravings because I was still getting the nicotine my body was used to, but in much smaller and therefore less harmful doses, and without the added harmful effects of cigarette smoke.

What I have found difficult, though (and this is why it is crucial to follow each step of Chris' plan), is to break the habits surrounding my smoking. Getting into the car, for instance, was a vulnerable moment for me because I had always lit up as soon as I drove anywhere. What you've got to do is to prepare for these vulnerable moments and try to occupy not only your hands but your mind as well. You can change these habits, but it takes a conscious and positive effort to do so.

I have been surprised at how easy stopping smoking has been. You can't do it by cutting down, and you are making life so much more difficult than you need to if you don't help yourself by using nicotine chewing gum. So use the gum, and make your commitment to stopping smoking now - take the advice in Chris' *Smokers' Quit Plan* because it really can work for you.

Sean Sullivan

Let's hope that you are now inspired and you might even be feeling a little tingle of anticipation at the thought of being free of cigarettes. As an ex-smoker of 40 a day for 15 years, I would say it is worth it. Life is easier without cigarettes, not to mention cheaper, more pleasant and healthier. Stopping smoking is a life project which needs careful planning and preparation, a lot of support and a lot of positive thinking - but it may save your life!

CHAPTER SIX

DEALING WITH DEPRESSION

DEALING WITH DEPRESSION

Depression is a difficult word to define because it is used to describe more than one condition. It can, for instance, refer more generally to mood; or more specifically to indicate an illness which prevents a person from functioning normally and which requires active treatment. One great difficulty with depression is that sufferers are often unaware that they are depressed, and even if they are aware, they are often either too frightened to seek help or they don't know where to find that help.

DEPRESSIVE ILLNESS

Depression can be an illness - but the good news is that it is very treatable. Although people in general are becoming more enlightened about the problem of depression, many still perceive it as some kind of weakness - this includes the sufferers themselves. The fact is, depressive illness can be so debilitating that it can disrupt daily living, family life, and work. If you're suffering from depression, you may develop physical symptoms, and your sense of helplessness and powerlessness may be overwhelming. Your feelings of sadness, pessimism and hopelessness are unlikely to be lifted by someone telling you robustly that everything will be OK, you must look on the bright side!

Everyone will, at some stage in their lives, feel significantly sad, disappointed or despairing. Things happen in our lives which bring about these understandable feelings and reactions, if someone you care about dies, for instance; or you lose your job; or your marriage breaks up. The feelings you experience as a result of these events are normal.

DEALING WITH DEPRESSION

REMEMBER

*Feeling sad does not
necessarily mean
you are depressed*

So what's the difference between feeling sad and being depressed?

- **depression lasts longer**
- **depression disrupts daily life**
- **depression is more intensely painful**
- **depression is destructive**
- **depression makes you self-critical**
- **depression is isolating and frightening**

Severe depression is more common than you probably think. One in five people will experience severe depression at some time in their lives and one in 15 will need hospital treatment for their depression. It is important to remember that many people who suffer from depression experience a combination of symptoms and that this list is just an example of some of the symptoms you may experience and recognise. Similarly, if you feel a bit tired occasionally, or irritable now and again, this doesn't necessarily mean you are depressed. When you are depressed, these symptoms combine to overwhelm you and may prevent you from functioning normally in daily life.

TYPES OF DEPRESSION

The following descriptions of **reactive** and **endogenous** depression are separated only for the purpose of explanation - the symptoms of each can combine, and sometimes reactive depression can become endogenous.

REACTIVE DEPRESSION

This is the milder form of depression. I am glad to say that this form of depression is the more common and although one in five of us will feel depressed at some stage in our lives, the depression is more likely to take this form than the more severe type.

DEALING WITH DEPRESSION

- *apathy,
indifference,
fatigue*
- *loss of interest in
daily life, lack of
enthusiasm*
- *increased
sensitivity to
criticism*
- *low self-esteem,
feelings of
inadequacy, loss
of confidence*
- *irritability,
frustration, anger*
- *feelings of guilt,
increased
tendency to
blame yourself*
- *feelings of
powerlessness
and hopelessness*
- *insomnia*
- *feelings of
extreme anxiety*
- *tendency to
wake up early in
the morning
feeling anxious*
- *poor
concentration/
forgetfulness*
- *drug/alcohol
abuse*
- *extreme mood
swings*
- *loss of sexual
appetite*
- *extreme weight
gain/loss*
- *overwhelming
desire to sleep all
the time*

The symptoms of reactive depression are thought to be caused by some tangible, external event which causes stress. This could be bereavement, unemployment, divorce and so on. As its name implies, your depression is a reaction to an event which provokes depressive symptoms. This depressive reaction is assumed to be reasonable and linked to the trauma which caused it.

It must be remembered, however, that the trigger for reactive depression does not have to be some major event. What is perceived as trivial stress can sometimes provoke a depressive reaction too. Although considered to be the milder form of depression, this type can also deteriorate into a more severe state of depression.

ENDOGENOUS DEPRESSION

This is the more severe type of depression and is assumed to come from within the person, with no obvious trigger event. As such, the sufferer will often deny to themselves and to their doctor that any depressive symptoms exist. A common feature of severe depression is that the intensity of depressive feelings do fluctuate throughout the day. Commonly, depression is worse in the morning. Through the day it will improve and, sometimes, may become less evident by evening. Severe or endogenous depression is something in which your mood changes significantly through stages of sadness and misery to utter despair and hopelessness. These mood changes combine with a decreased energy level and an inability to concentrate on or perform daily tasks. There is an overall loss of interest in things and people around you. In some cases, the memory ceases to function as well as in the past and this can be the most frightening symptom of all.

DEALING WITH DEPRESSION

Depression can creep up on you without you realising it. One of the crucial aspects of helping yourself is understanding yourself. The concept of reactive depression is understandably less alarming than the more severe endogenous depression. If you know that you are depressed because someone you love has died, or left you, then you have a real reason for your feelings. But if you are experiencing symptoms of severe depression for apparently no reason, it can be very distressing.

With severe depression, sufferers often don't seek treatment until their symptoms become physically manifest. As such, given mood fluctuations, when they visit their doctor sometimes only the physical symptoms are evident. For different reasons, the patient might only tell the doctor about the physical symptoms and may be so convincing that the doctor may not be able to perceive the underlying depressive illness.

CAUSES OF DEPRESSION

Although the exact cause of depression is not known, many different factors have been identified which may contribute to feelings of depression.

1. GENETIC FACTORS
There is no evidence that genetic factors contribute to reactive depression, but it has been found that close relatives (brothers, sisters, parents and children) of people suffering from severe depressive illness have a greater risk (approximately 10%-15%) of also suffering from depressive illness. There are conflicting theories about this cause of depression, however, as the available evidence is scientifically unreliable. The main conclusion researchers have come to is that whilst it is probable that

genetic inheritance makes us more prone to depression, it has not yet been proven.

2. BIOLOGICAL DEPRESSION

Sometimes depression is caused by biological factors. The hypothalamus and limbic systems working within the brain play major roles in regulating not only our biological cycles, but our emotions too. The hypothalamus is the control centre for, amongst other things, the immune system and the hormonal system. It also controls our physical activities such as sleeping, sexual drives, appetite and the ability to experience pleasure. The limbic system is sometimes referred to as the 'emotional brain' as it helps to control our emotional output. For instance, if you are faced with a painful and stressful event such as bereavement, the limbic system (if working correctly) will control the intensity of your feelings.

Both the hypothalamus and limbic system function properly when there is a balance of various neurochemicals in the brain. Sometimes this balance is disrupted and when this happens, you may experience biological depression. Four things can cause chemical imbalances:

a/ Medication

If you are taking medication, the side-effects of the drug may cause a chemical imbalance in the brain which can trigger biological depression. This is very rare. But if you are taking medication and you can find no tangible reason for your depression, you should contact your GP as soon as possible.

b/ Drug/alcohol abuse

Long-term drug users, whilst experiencing a 'high' from drugs such as cocaine and amphetamines, will also experience serious depressive symptoms when they 'come down' again. More common than this is the long term abuse of alcohol which cannot only cause social, family ad emotional problems but which is also a cerebral depressant drug which in itself provokes or prolongs depression.

c/ Physical illness

This can produce depressive symptoms for two reasons. The illness itself may result in chemical changes within the brain; sometimes, though, the patient may suffer from psychological depression about the illness itself.

d/ Hormonal changes

Post-natal depression, pre-menstrual tension and menopause are not physical illnesses but are conditions which involve significant hormonal changes. It is believed that such hormonal changes can disrupt the delicate balance of chemicals in the brain and therefore can lead to biological depression.

3. STRESS

Stress caused by an individual's reaction to certain events can cause depression to set in. Stress can come from any situation; it could be moving house, bereavement, changing school, retirement, money problems - anything at all. Stress is very subjective. It could be that whilst one person thrives on changing jobs frequently, or moving house, another person finds that same situation stressful. Accompanying all of these stressful situations is a potential sense of loss, of having to leave something behind; this usually results in feelings of grief. Grief can be a very healthy emotion, leading to positive recovery. But 10-15% of us who feel grief of some kind will go on to become depressed. (See Chapter on **Stress** for more details.)

4. CHILDHOOD EXPERIENCES

Traumatic experiences as a child can sometimes lead to depression in later life, if that child has suppressed his or her feelings about the event. It may help to explain why you are experiencing certain feelings now if you look back and try and identify similar feelings from your childhood. Traumatic childhood experiences and feelings which have been suppressed over the years, can contribute to the development of depression in adult life.

Sometimes the reasons for depression seem clear. There are many situations and events which, in our society, are accepted reasons for being depressed. People will allow you to be depressed if you are recently bereaved, for instance, or if you have just gone through a divorce. But often the reason for your depression is far from clear both to yourself and to those around you; they will feel confused when you are showing symptoms of depression because they too probably won't recognise what the symptoms mean. Those closest to you, such as family members and close friends, will feel insecure as a result of your depression.

Assume, for instance, that you are in a family situation. You are depressed. You have lost interest in sex. You have lost all enthusiasm for your child's school activities. You have lost interest in your appearance. You want to sleep most of the time. You are irritable. You cry a lot.

You have become insular, preferring to talk as little as possible. Understandably, your family will feel as perplexed as you do yourself about your feelings and your changed behaviour. You probably haven't told them how you're feeling - the despair, the sense of hopelessness, the utter misery - because you may feel that you should be happy. You have apparently no reason for being depressed and consequently feel guilty about your feelings. But the people around you are not mind-readers. You need their support and, as well as seeking professional treatment, it may help to tell your husband or your children (if they're old enough) how you are feeling. If you don't tell them anything, they will feel excluded and antagonistic towards you which in turn will make you withdraw even further.

Depression is a very complex area and can be mild or severe, it can be caused by biological or psychological factors or a combination of the two. Defining and diagnosing depression is not a clear cut issue, and although I have listed reactive depression and endogenous depression as two different forms of illness, they are not necessarily separate.

TREATING DEPRESSION

The majority of people suffering from depression receive absolutely no treatment whatsoever. This is partly due to the negative feelings surrounding the subject. Although information about depression is increasingly available, many people still refuse to see it as an illness. Many people actually interpret symptoms of depression as products of self-indulgence, weakness and laziness - hard to believe, isn't it? People find depression a frightening issue and so refuse to think about it or discuss it. Many people who may be depressed will feel unable to discuss it with anybody, including their doctor. Some people may not even realise that depression is the reason for the way they are feeling. Many people, whilst knowing that they are depressed, may not know that help is available. Many people who are depressed may feel such an overwhelming sense of hopelessness that they think they'll never get rid of the depression. This can become a vicious circle of self-neglect because the hopelessness is in itself a symptom of depression and can prevent the sufferer from seeking help.

REMEMBER

The feeling of hopelessness can be relieved

With the right form of treatment, most people can overcome this feeling of hopelessness and other symptoms of depression.

WHAT SORT OF TREATMENT IS AVAILABLE?

There are two main areas of treatment - professional and self-help approaches.

1.PROFESSIONAL TREATMENT - MEDICAL

If you are depressed and suffering from consequent physical symptoms, you should consult your GP. Sometimes your doctor will prescribe anti-depressant medication to help you with your depression. There is a widespread misapprehension about anti-depressant medication. Anti-depressant medications are not tranquilisers. Many people assume that they are one and the same thing - this is not true. As such, people are frightened of becoming addicted to medication given to help with depression.

Anti-depressants, unlike some tranquilisers, are not addictive. Anti-depressants help to ease the intensity of emotional pain, and they eliminate many of the biological symptoms of depression such as sleep problems. Anti-depressants can also restore your ability to experience pleasure, but they cannot produce feelings of happiness. Anti-depressants produce lasting changes by restoring parts of the nervous system to a state of natural and normal functioning. Use them to feel better initially - they cannot cure your problem completely, but they help to restore a basic sense of well-being so that you can help yourself to feel better. Even if they only help you to sleep better, being less tired means that you will be better able to deal with the rest of the problem.

Anti-depressant medications can take from 10-21 days to start working. The reason for this is that it simply takes that long for the medication to begin to reverse the biological imbalance and to restore malfunctioning nerve cells to their normal state. Such medications have been found to be effective in 75% of properly diagnosed cases.

Things to remember about anti-depressant medication
a/ side-effects are possible
b/ positive effects are not immediately noticeable
c/ medication can treat the biological aspects of depression but does not treat the psychological symptoms

The third point is very important. Anti-depressants cannot solve your problem altogether. They can help you to deal with the initial physical symptoms of your depression but the underlying problems must be dealt

DEALING WITH DEPRESSION

with as well. Anti-depressants are a very useful way of starting to deal with your depression - they restore your physiological well-being, not necessarily your psychological well being.

SIDE-EFFECTS OF ANTI-DEPRESSANT MEDICATION

SIDE EFFECTS THAT CAN OCCUR

- *dry mouth*
- *slight blurring of vision*
- *dizziness or faintness*
- *sweating*
- *constipation*
- *drowsiness*

Side effects may occur within two days of beginning the course of medication. Most of these side-effects can be dealt with either by changing to another anti-depressant, or by a reduction in the dosage.

If you are in any doubt about your medication, discuss it with your GP and decide together whether this is the right form of treatment for you.

KNOW YOUR ANTI-DEPRESSANTS

There are many types of anti-depressant drug. The main ones prescribed are called tricyclic anti-depressants. They are called tricyclic because of their chemical structure which comprises three or more rings.

Sedative Effect	Less Sedative	Stimulant	New Anti-Depressants
AMITRIPTLINE	BUTRIPTYLINE	PROTRIPTYLINE	FLUOXETINE
DOTHIEPIN	CLOMIPRAMINE		FLUVOXAMINE
DOXEPIN	DESIPRAMINE		
MAPROFILINE	IMIPRAMINE		(Both of these new anti-depressants produce no effects of sedation or stimulation, so ask your GP whether they are suitable forms of treatment for you.)
MIANSERIN	IPRINDOLE		
TRAZODONE	LOFEPRAMINE		
TRIMIPRAMINE	NORTRIPTYLINE		
	VILOXAZINE		

Daunting as this complex list of anti-depressants may seem, it is included to reassure you - so if you do

REMEMBER

Tranquilisers are not the same as anti-depressant medication

develop unpleasant side effects from your particular prescribed anti-depressant, this medication can be changed to eradicate those side effects. There are many different types of anti-depressant. It may take some time before the right drug at the right dosage level is found to relieve symptoms. Ask your doctor to tell you which benefits and side effects you might expect.

2. PROFESSIONAL TREATMENT - PSYCHOLOGICAL

If you are depressed, go to your GP first of all. Your doctor can help you to realise whether your depression is due to biological or psychological factors, or a combination of the two. If it is due to biological factors, then your doctor can describe some anti-depressant medication. As anti-depressants cannot solve the whole problem, you may also benefit from some form of psychotherapy also. If your depression is purely psychological, then psychological treatment is best for you.

What is psychotherapy? Basically, any treatment which doesn't involve medication can be called psychotherapy. Your doctor can refer you to a psychotherapist if necessary. Be aware, however, that recognising depressive illness can be difficult for both patients and doctors. Before you visit your doctor, therefore, make a list of your symptoms and write down your feelings. This will enable you to communicate with your doctor as efficiently as possible - with a clearer understanding between you, an accurate diagnosis is more likely.

Many people think that if they're depressed they're going mad. Being depressed does not mean that you're going mad. But you cannot usually cope with depression on

REMEMBER

Don't be frightened about the idea of therapy

your own. Therapists are trained to help you to overcome your depression. Use them. The most important aspect of psychotherapy is talking about your feelings. Many people find it easier to discuss their feelings with someone who has a professional and objective perception of their situation. One woman I spoke to said that she felt easier talking to a therapist than to members of her family because she didn't feel guilty about expressing her feelings.

There are different schools of thought amongst psychotherapists, each one putting a slightly different emphasis on important phases and events in your life. The varying ideas behind the therapy determine the way the therapy is applied and the relationship between the therapist and the patient.

WHAT'S THE DIFFERENCE BETWEEN A PSYCHIATRIST AND A PSYCHOLOGIST?

PSYCHIATRISTS are medical doctors who specialise in treating emotional problems. In addition to psychological treatment they can provide medical treatment if it is needed.

PSYCHOLOGISTS have a degree in psychology, plus usually 3-4 years postgraduate training in psychological methods. They are also specially trained in the administration and interpretation of psychological tests.

SOME EXAMPLES OF WIDELY AVAILABLE PSYCHOTHERAPY

Cognitive Therapy

This is a relatively new form of psychological treatment. It is based on the theory that depressive moods are caused by negative thinking. So, for instance, if you are depressed, you will be manifesting symptoms of what therapists call the cognitive triad - this is a negative view of yourself, a negative interpretation of your experiences and a negative view of the future. There are two aspects to this theory. Firstly, feelings of low self-esteem, self-criticism and self-blame are common in depression. These feelings and thoughts predominate during depression. Secondly, there are cognitive distortions. This means that our thinking and understanding of reality are distorted. In other words, our perception of reality is distorted to the point that we fully believe our feelings of low self-esteem, self-criticism and self-blame. However irrational these feelings may be, cognitive distortions make us perceive them as the reality.

How does cognitive therapy work?

Because it is based on the idea that the way we think determines our emotions and our behaviour, cognitive therapy aims to make the patient aware of his or her negative and destructive way of thinking. This form of therapy contrasts with the more traditional view of therapy which sees negative thinking as a result of depression, rather than as a cause. A cognitive therapist will help you to undo your pattern of negative thinking by making you examine the evidence which contradicts your negative ideas. You will be encouraged to challenge your own underlying assumptions about yourself and the way you expect people to treat you. The therapist will take you through a sort of checklist of problem solving:

A **Defining the problem**
B **Dividing the problem into manageable parts**
C **Thinking of alternative solutions**

D Selecting the best solution for you

E Putting the solution into effect

F Examining the result

Role playing is found to be a useful way of achieving this awareness and recognition of links between negative thinking and depression.

The therapist will also train you to look at different situations in different ways. Once you have become used to thinking of alternative ways of interpreting events, the therapist may encourage you to keep a sort of mood diary in which you record your different moods and the feelings which accompany them. You may be asked to offer alternative interpretations of your own moods. You will be encouraged to put your negative beliefs and attitudes to the test. This will train you discover the truth through inquiry instead of assumption.

Cognitive therapy is not easy, but I believe it is an excellent form of treatment. The therapist cannot solve your problems or cure your depression for you: in any case to do that would be of little help to you. What this form of therapy does do, however, is to help you to help yourself by teaching you to understand yourself. Cognitive therapy usually works in approximately 15 sessions over a three-month period and, depending on the therapist's decision about the best situation for you the therapy may be on a one to one basis or take place within a group situation.

Behaviour therapy

This form of therapy often takes procedures from cognitive therapy but their specific expertise stresses techniques such as activity therapy, assertiveness training and behaviour monitoring. The behavioural therapist will aim to get you moving again, focusing on the tendency when depressed to withdraw and close down activity perhaps by setting you simple activity tasks such as attending a lecture or going to see a concert - this sort of activity doesn't require much active participation from the individual but it will ease the transition back to normal social life and will help to gradually rebuild the person's capacity for enjoyment. Another technique may be to gradually expose the individual to feared situations, whilst helping that person to reduce the anxiety connected with the situation.

Transactional analysis

This form of therapy is based on a simple theory about human interaction. It suggests that every individual has three subpersonalities - the Parent, the Adult, the Child. The Parent is the part of us which both internally criticises us, but also supports and nourishes us. The Child part enables us to be spontaneously happy or disobedient. The Adult is the wise and realistic part of us. Transactional analysis, then, examines how the three parts of us co-exist and interact. It also examines how we interact with other people when different parts of us meets different parts of others - for instance, when the child in you meets the child in someone else, you could end up helpless with laughter. But if the child in you meets the parent in someone else, you may annoy the other person and they will be critical of you.

The key phrase in transactional analysis is, 'I'm OK, you're OK!' - that is when all parts of us respond to others on an equally respectful level. Thinking too highly of ourselves whilst criticising others would be 'I'm OK, you're not OK'; and putting ourselves down by elevating others would be, 'You're OK, I'm not OK.'

If you opt for this kind of treatment, you will be taught how to use this theory to analyse what is happening within you and in your relationships with others. You will gain valuable insight from this about yourself and you will be able to change destructive notions and assumptions with can cause depression.

Hypnotherapy

Hypnotherapists would take time to find out what your goals are and check they likely to make you feel better If there is some conflict in this area, hypnotherapists believe that your subconscious is unlikely to cooperate. There are many misapprehensions about hypnotherapy; it is unlikely that a hypnotherapist will use a bright object to focus your attention. What is more likely is that you will be encouraged to relax and allow your mind to become calm. Then the therapist will address your subconscious mind directly, asking it to help in the effort to achieve your goals. You may remember everything that has happened during a hypnotherapy session, and then again, you may not. Whether you remember is not a sign of the effectiveness of the hypnotherapy. It is vital here, though, that you make sure you are working with a trained and ethical practitioner. also remember that with this form of therapy, there is no scope for talking or becoming emotional with your therapist.

These, then, are just a sample of the numerous schools of psychotherapeutic thought. If you want to find out more about the available options please refer to the **Useful Information** section.

CHAPTER SEVEN

STRESS~SYMPTOMS
AND SOLUTIONS

CHAPTER SEVEN

STRESS – SYMPTOMS AND SOLUTIONS

WHAT IS STRESS?

Stress is the term used to describe psychological and physical pressure on an individual. We know that our minds and bodies are closely linked. So when you are in a situation which your mind perceives as stressful, this information will be transmitted to your body's nervous system. The nervous system will make adjustments to your physical functions so that your energy level is increased to enable you to cope more efficiently with those extra demands. Adrenalin pumps into the bloodstream, your heart rate increases, your blood pressure rises, blood sugar is released, your muscles become tense and your breathing becomes shallow. So if you are in a dangerous situation, for instance, the physical adjustments your body has made will enable you to run away from that danger.

EXAMPLE:

Person crossing the road

Sees lorry hurtling towards her

Feeling of stress

Stress produces increased energy level

Person can run fast to avoid being hit

As you can see, then, from this example, a certain amount of stress is good. And not just for those extreme and dangerous situations. Some stress in our lives is necessary and beneficial - without it we would find it very difficult to get going and feel motivated. The surge of adrenalin we feel in a stressful situation can enable us to increase our performance and to think efficiently. Stress becomes harmful and counterproductive, however, when it reaches excessive and intolerable levels and when it damages our sense of psychological and physical well-being.

And stress means different things to different people - situations which I find stressful, for instance, may involve no stress at all for someone else. Like many other problems in life, many people assume that stress is only an external phenomenon which is thrust upon us in certain situations. As such, many believe that stress is uncontrollable and inevitable. This is not always the case. Although there are situations which are in themselves stressful, it is more likely to be an individual's reaction to a situation which produces stress, not the situation itself. If stress were an inevitable part of certain situations then it follows that everyone would react in the same way. If you perceive a job interview, for instance, as a difficult and threatening situation, you will perform in the interview accordingly. You will feel stressed. However, if you can learn to see the interview as a positive challenge, you are far less likely to experience overwhelming stress in that situation. Following the guidelines in Chapter One, you can use your imagination to avoid the self-fulfilling prophecy of stress. Self-fulfilling prophecy refers to the circle of belief, expectation and reality. You imagine that an interview is stressful, you expect the interview to be stressful, the interview is stressful. If you imagine the interview to be enjoyable and stimulating, you will expect it to be so, and it will be enjoyable and stimulating.

REMEMBER:

You can't control external events but you can control your reaction to them

Recognising the warning signs is vital. Stress is cumulative - one incident or situation is not going to suddenly change you from a calm and relaxed person into one suffering from the effects of stress. Stress is produced when problems are left unsolved and allowed to build and grow until they seem collectively impossible to cope with. Think what would happen, for instance, if you never had your car serviced - problems would go undetected and eventually the car would break down. But most people do have their cars serviced regularly so that potential problems are detected before they even happen.

STRESS – SYMPTOMS AND SOLUTIONS

PHYSICAL
SYMPTOMS:

- *dizziness,
  nausea, vomiting*
- *heart
  palpitations, or
  missing a beat*
- *chest pains*
- *excessive
  sweating*
- *headaches*
- *backaches*
- *stiff limbs*
- *dry mouth*
- *butterflies in the
  stomach*
- *trembling*
- *breathing
  difficulties*
- *muscle tension*
- *overwhelming
  tiredness*

*BEHAVIOURAL
SYMPTOMS:*

- *excessive irritability*
- *excessive smoking
  and/or drinking*
- *inability to
  concentrate*
- *staying off work*
- *working too hard*
- *avoiding people
  and/or situations*
- *loss of sexual
  appetite*
- *overeating*
- *not eating enough*

Taking steps to avoid problems with stress should be as regular and as automatic as that.

SYMPTOMS OF STRESS

Just as your car may have a red warning light to indicate that something is wrong, these symptoms are your warning lights. If you do experience any of these symptoms and there is no medical reason for them, then you must learn to deal with the problem before it gets out of hand.

RELAXATION EXERCISE

1. Find a quiet, private place where you can sit down.
2. Sit comfortably with both feet on the floor a few inches apart and your arms unfolded and relaxed.
3. Breathe in slowly and deeply. As you breathe out, close your eyes.
4. Breathe in again. As you breathe out, unclench your teeth.
5. Breathe in again. As you breathe out, let your shoulders drop.
6. Breathe in again. As you breathe out, unclench your fists.
7. Breathe in again. Hold the breath for five seconds. Now breathe out. Repeat this 5-10 times.

This exercise allows oxygen to reach your brain. You can think more clearly because you are physically and mentally more relaxed. When you are feeling stressed everything in your body tightens up and therefore doesn't function as it should; this may affect your muscles and your breathing apparatus. The less oxygen your brain gets, the less efficiently it works.

STRESS – SYMPTOMS AND SOLUTIONS

There are certain commonly experienced situations which are perceived as stressful in themselves. Here we are into the old self-fulfilling prophecy rut again. If, for instance, you are told frequently that, to use the same example, job interviews are threatening, then that is how you will perceive them and you may experience the stress because of your anticipation of stress.

Having said that, there are certain situations which you will encounter in your life which are more difficult to deal with than others. This does not necessarily mean that you will be stressed. If you can discover what makes you feel bad, and take steps to deal with those feelings, then you are less likely to display symptoms of stress.

WORK CAN PRODUCE STRESS

Many people associate feelings of stress with their work. Feeling stressed because of your work can have far-reaching consequences as these feelings may impinge on your home life too. If you are one of these people and you think you cannot cope with your work, stop and ask yourself why you cannot cope. Is it because:

A/ you are disorganised?

B/ you do not have enough time to do your work?

C/ you have too much responsibility?

D/ you have to work such long hours?

E/ you are having problems with colleagues?

A/ BEING ORGANISED

If you think disorganisation is contributing to your difficulties at work, see becoming organised as a positive step to reducing your feelings of stress. If you are not a naturally organised person, make lists to help you to remember things. Have an in-tray and an out-tray so that you know where you're up to with your work. At the beginning or end of each day, sort through the trays. Put away things you have dealt with, and make a list from your in-tray of things which need your attention that day. Up-date your lists twice a day - you'd be surprised at the amount of satisfaction you will feel when you are able to cross things off the list.

NOTE:

Don't rely on others to remind you to do things

Relying on someone else to remind you of something is a way of avoiding your responsibilities - after all, if they forget you can always blame them, can't you? Just think how much more competent and in control of your work you will feel when you can always find that file or that letter at a minute's notice.

B/ NOT ENOUGH TIME

Be realistic about what you can achieve in one day or one week. If your boss sets what you think are unrealistic goals, don't object immediately. Go away and think about what you have been asked to do and by when. Make a schedule or a plan of how you can achieve those goals, listing all the little jobs which will be necessary along the way to achieving the required end. There are two solutions to this problem. You may be able to see a way of completing the task in the required time by having some help from a colleague. If you know that there will be nobody available to help you and you feel that the only solution is to have a little more time in which to do the job, then work out how much time will be needed and offer an alternative deadline. Both these solutions mean that you can go back to your boss with a positive response. A sensible boss will appreciate your initiative and foresight and is therefore likely to agree to your proposition.

If you don't do these things, however, and accept the given deadline, you will end up feeling stressed. You will feel that you cannot cope, and you won't get the job done on time anyway! Just remember that you are not superman or woman and nobody expects you to be.

C/ TOO MUCH RESPONSIBILITY

If you feel that this is why you are feeling under stress and this feeling of stress is obliterating any enjoyment of the job, you must decide two things. Firstly, are you feeling like this because you're in the wrong job? Answer honestly - it may have seemed like a wonderful step up the career ladder when you took the job, but perhaps aspects of the job are not complementary to aspects of your personality. List the positive and negative aspects of, for instance, your current job.

It may be that although you appreciate the higher salary, company car and good prospects of your current position, you dislike the travelling and the fact that you have to regularly head meetings and conferences. If this is the case, then you should seriously consider removing yourself from this situation.

Secondly, if you have decided that there are enough positive aspects to your job to remain there, ask yourself why the sense of responsibility is provoking a stressful response from you. Is it because you are lacking in confidence? It is unlikely that your employer has made a mistake when you were given the job. You will have displayed qualities both in your previous job and in your interview which will have indicated to your employer that you are able to handle the extra responsibility of your new position. Also consider the possibility that other people may have been off-loading their responsibilities onto you in the knowledge that you will, by hook or by crook, get the job done well and on time. This process can be very subtle, so beware!

D/ LONG HOURS

If you are showing signs of stress because you are consistently expected to work from 7.30 am until late at night, ask yourself the following questions:

- **is it because I am disorganised that I am taking longer to do the work?**
- **should I have an assistant?**
- **am I trying to impress the boss by staying late?**
- **should I be pursuing a different line of work?**

If you can answer **YES** to any of these questions, then take steps to effect whatever change is necessary. If you are disorganised, then you can become more organised; if you are working to your full potential and you still feel you need help, present your case in a positive and helpful way to your boss - don't apologise for not being able to do everything yourself; if you are trying to impress by working long hours, you are wasting your time. Sensible employers won't want their staff to exhaust themselves unnecessarily.

E/ PROBLEMS WITH COLLEAGUES

If you are unhappy at work because of your relationships with your colleagues, there are a number of positive steps you can take to improve the situation. If you feel that they tend to shirk their responsibilities and that you are doing the lion's share of the work, talk to them about it. Be pleasant and firm and suggest ways in which you can all split the workload. You are discuss- ing a work issue and it should not be a personal matter.

Remember that we often cannot choose our colleagues and sometimes people will do things or behave in a way which could cause problems. Remember that you can't control other people's behaviour, but you can control your reaction to it.

HOME LIFE CAN BE STRESSFUL

Everyone comes to you with their problems, practical and emotional. Despite having a full-time job, you are the one who has to remember to set all the alarm clocks so that You are the one who remembers everybody's birthdays and buys all the presents. You have to plead with others in the house to help with the chores. You are frequently told how wonderful you are, what a saint you are and how nobody could cope without you.

Is this you? If it is, whilst you might enjoy the sporadic but flattering comments, it is likely that you are feeling some degree of stress. When do you ever have time to fulfil your own needs and express your own feelings? Never, is the likely answer. As a consequence, you may be feeling resentful towards the other members of the family who so happily take from you without seeming to want to give back. These feelings of resentment are often accompanied by pangs of guilt that you are a bad mother or a bad wife for feeling resentful. If you suppress these feelings you are likely to become stressed. But you can stop it all before it reaches that stage:

- **realise that your family will love you even if you refuse their demands now and again.**
- **you have rights, needs and desires which should be**

fulfilled so allocate some time for doing exactly what you want to do. If someone tries to interrupt and make demands on you, tell them that you are doing something else now and can't they do it themselves or get help elsewhere?

- call a family meeting. Discuss how you can share the chores more evenly between you. Explain that you are feeling annoyed because you are carrying the whole load.
- allow yourself to feel angry. They won't run away simply because you express your true feelings.
- make demands on them. If your children are old enough, talk to them about your feelings. Tell them what your likes and dislikes are. You'll probably become a much more interesting person to them and more than just 'a mother'.
- don't use emotional blackmail - don't use statements like 'after all I've done for you.' because this is counterproductive. It also indicates that your motives for doing all those things need examination. Were you looking for more love by doing all those things for them all? Love isn't earned in this way. They will love you anyway for who you are, not what you do for them.

The crux of any relationship is the degree of give and take involved. If one person is giving all the time and the other is taking, the relationship is likely to be stressful to one or both partners. Most people don't want to take all the time. So give them the opportunity to do things for you too. Expressing your anger or your disappointment tells the other person that you have faith in your relationship. And remember that people aren't mind-readers. If you are showing signs of stress and you

STRESS – SYMPTOMS AND SOLUTIONS

haven't expressed your feelings to that other person or people, they will only feel baffled at your behaviour. Give them the chance to understand you and you are less likely to feel stressed.

STRESS SUMMARY

REMEMBER:

You are what you imagine yourself to be

Only you can determine your own level of stress. It is up to you whether you become a positive thinker and help yourself counteract potential stress or whether you take an ostrich approach to problematic situations and allow yourself to become stressed.

DEALING WITH STRESS ~ THE LIFESTYLE DIARY

MONDAY

Overslept	*Felt anxious*
Travelled to work on crowded bus	*agitated by crowds*
Important meeting over lunch	*Indigestion*
Afternoon off - went shopping with friend	*Relaxed, content*
Evening - partner brought unexpected visitors home	*Felt angry and hostile*
Got to bed late - hard time getting to sleep	*Tired and anxious worried about over sleeping again*

Writing things down is an enormous help when you're making any changes in your life. So buy an exercise book and keep a record of your situations and the feelings accompanying them. Write down what you do each day for a week - next to each event and situation, describe how you felt at that time.

There are several things here that can be dealt with and your stress level reduced.

1. SLEEP PROBLEMS

Sleep patterns can be disturbed for many reasons and just as not getting the regular healthy sleep that you need can be part of the cause of your feelings of stress, so can lack of sleep be a symptom too. Try these tips for a healthy night's sleep:

- **if you are experiencing disturbed sleep on a regular basis, and there is no apparent medical reason, think about whether there is a problem in your life which is causing you to feel stressed or depressed. You'll find that if you can put that right, your sleep problems will resolve themselves too.**
- **have a relaxing bath just before going to bed. The water should be lukewarm - very hot or very cold water may act as a stimulant.**
- **avoid drinks of tea or coffee late at night. The caffeine in them is a stimulant and may keep you awake.**
- **make sure the bedroom isn't too stuffy.**
- **a drink of warm milk really will help to relax you before you go to sleep - it's not just an old wives' tale!**
- **try the relaxation exercise provided earlier**
- **establish a going to bed routine - this will establish a link between your conscious actions and your subconscious expectations. If you expect to sleep, you probably will be able to sleep.**
- **don't worry about being able to wake up. The anxiety produced by too much worry will in itself prevent you from sleeping well. If necessary, get two reliable alarm clocks and set one to go off 10 minutes after the first.**

The fact of oversleeping itself will set you on the wrong footing for the whole day. You will be panicking about being late for work, you will rush around getting ready and probably won't have enough time for breakfast.

2. TRAVEL

There may not be anything you can do about how you travel to work, but you can do something about the way it makes you feel. If your train or bus is always crowded, try getting to the station or bus stop a little earlier than normal. If you've run all the way to the bus stop, just caught the bus by the skin of your teeth and then you have to stand for 20 minutes, you're not going to be able to feel relaxed. If you travel to work by car, perhaps the traffic jams make you feel stressed. If so, try listening to your favourite soothing music on the car stereo. Above all, if you can't change the situation, Don't waste energy getting angry because it will only make you feel worse. You cannot control when the bus comes but you can control your feelings.

3. AVOIDING TENSION AT WORK

Being punctual, well-organised and feeling prepared will all prevent unnecessary feelings of tension at those frequent lunch meetings, and therefore will prevent that unpleasant indigestion. Being a few minutes early for a meeting can give you time to relax and gather your thoughts. Make a list before the meeting about points you want to raise. If you find eating and discussing items on the agenda a problem, see if you can suggest another way of having the meeting, perhaps having the meeting first and the lunch afterwards. Or perhaps you can forget lunch altogether and have the meeting back at the office?

4. THE EVENING

Things will always happen in our lives over which we appear to have no control. So what should you do when your partner appears with three unexpected guests for the evening? Above all don't waste time feeling hostile, angry and resentful - it really won't achieve anything except that you will feel much much worse than you did in the first place. Maybe spend an hour or two with them and explain that you are going to have an early night. If they don't take the hint and leave, let your partner continue with the socialising and go off and have your early night. If you don't do this, you will feel angry and resentful and will probably have a row with your partner after the guests have gone. Then you won't be able to sleep, and tomorrow may be as difficult as today was.

Allow yourself to be happy and relaxed. If you are pleasant and reasonable, no-one will criticise you for doing what you need to do to keep your peace of mind and avoid feeling stressed. And take positive steps to avoid this sort of thing happening again.

TERRIE: *LIFEGUIDE* MEMBER

Terrie is in her 50s. She runs a small business which means she works hard six days a week. Terrie joined Lifeguide because she had a nagging feeling that life had more to offer than just work. She felt that her business had taken over her life and that she needed some more time for herself. As with the other women in the group, joining Lifeguide in the first place was a positive step for Terrie. She has acknowledged that she has been a workaholic and was not controlling the direction of her life.

Terrie says, 'Because of Lifeguide and through meeting all the other women and listening to their problems and talking about mine, I have been able to make positive decisions about my life because I am feeling more confident. I'm resolving the problem of working constantly and making a conscious effort to do the things I want to do.'

CHAPTER EIGHT

WORK~RETURNING TO PAID EMPLOYMENT

CHAPTER EIGHT

WORK ~ RETURNING TO PAID EMPLOYMENT

CHANGING PERCEPTIONS OF WOMEN'S WORK

There's one point I'd like to clarify before we begin this important section of the book - if you decide to take a job outside the home after a period away from paid employment you are not simply, as many would say, *returning* to work. You *have* been working all the time - bringing up your children, cleaning the house, managing the accounts, and organising the family. You are probably a DIY expert, a chef, a seamstress and an interior designer into the bargain! So you are redirecting your skills and talents and taking them outside the home and into the workforce. By perceiving your work within the home as a positive experience, you will feel more positive about your future. Dismissing the skills you have acquired in the home will only undermine your self-confidence when you find a job elsewhere.

NOTE:

Positive thinking can boost your self-confidence!

Self-confidence, or lack of it, can be a major problem for women who decide to take a job outside the home after any period of time.

SCENARIO

Take Dorothy for example. She left school in 1966 with six O levels, completed a six-month secretarial course and worked for two years as a typist in a big industrial firm. She married in the late 60s and had three children in the first eight years of her marriage. As her husband earned enough money to support the whole family, Dorothy concentrated on bringing up her three children and managing the household. By the mid-80s, Dorothy felt that her children no longer needed her full-time attention, and two of them had already left home.

Although there was no financial necessity to do so she decided that she wanted to find another job outside the home. Now that the children were more or less grown up, her work at home was less stimulating. She was feeling bored. Having made the decision to find a job, Dorothy came up against two obstacles: her husband and her confidence. Her husband wasn't keen on the idea of Dorothy finding work outside the home and battling with her husband brought her self-confidence down. She decided that it had been a silly idea anyway - she couldn't do anything but cook and clean - so she abandoned her plans and resigned herself to finding stimulating activities she could do at home.

Your husband and children are an important factor, as you can see from this example, in your decision to find a job outside the home. Remember that if you effect any significant change in your lifestyle, the people around you may not like it. If you have been the emotional and practical support base for your family for as long as they can remember, they may feel threatened when you suggest a change.

MAKING THE DECISION TO FIND A JOB

1. **Decide why you want to find a job. Is it because you are bored, lonely or need the money? Or perhaps you have always had a burning ambition which you now have the time to try and fulfil?**
2. **What will the practical effect be on your family?**
3. **How do you think your husband and/or children will react to this lifestyle change?**
4. **If you cannot rely on them for support, do you have others you can turn to for practical and emotional help?**

5. When you start work, will you then in effect be doing two jobs - not only your 9-5 job but also the housework?

If life were perfect, you would be able to find your ideal job, and enlist the enthusiasm, help and support of your family in doing so. Unhappily, though, this ideal is more the exception than the rule judging by the letters we have received in the *Lifeguide* office. Here, then, are some tips on how to get the best possible reaction from your nearest and dearest:

- call a family meeting and tell them why you are going to find a job away from the home
- ask them how they feel about you doing this and stress the fact that you would appreciate not only their emotional and practical support, but their advice also
- point out the benefits to you and therefore to the family as a whole (more money, a more stimulating life for you).
- be firm but sympathetic with them. Understand that this big change of lifestyle may be difficult for them to cope with at first - but don't sacrifice your own needs and wishes for the sake of theirs.

Remember that, as with any other lifestyle change, there may be problems. Even if your family is supportive to you, there may be problems. Their emotional support alone is not enough - it would be unreasonable (although apparently fairly common) to be expected to work full-time outside the home, and to continue to run the household single-handedly. You will need the family to share more of the household duties. If there are four of you in the house who have full-time jobs, for instance, then it is reasonable to divide the housework into four areas of responsibility.

ASSESSING YOUR SKILLS AND BOOSTING YOUR CONFIDENCE

You must value yourself and your skills in order to succeed in the job market - after all, if you don't think you're any good at anything, how can you expect a potential employer to be persuaded to take you on? You are about to become a commodity in the job market and you must learn to value yourself in order to sell yourself to an employer. You wouldn't buy a product, for instance, if you didn't have any faith in it, would you? Well, nor would an employer give a job to someone in whom they had no faith!

'BUT I'M NOT GOOD AT ANYTHING!'

Everybody is good at something. All you have to do is recognise where your own talents lie. So first of all, make two separate lists detailing the jobs you normally do as part of your routine and your hobbies and interests.

Now you can make a true assessment of what you're good at and therefore what you are capable in the future of being good at. If you have been running a busy household for the last 15-20 years, for instance, you are probably an excellent manager. In fact you're probably so good at it that you make it look easy to others (hence their lack of recognition of your skills!). You balance the books, you organise your budget. You organise your menus and your food shopping according to that budget. You make sure bills are paid on time. You organise the cleaning, the washing and the ironing. You manage the

JOBS YOU
NORMALLY DO

~ *Cooking*
~ *Cleaning*
~ *Gardening*
~ *Sewing*
~ *Decorating*
~ *Driving*
~ *Shopping*
~ *Paying bills*

HOBBIES/
INTERESTS

~ *Sport*
~ *Reading*
~ *Writing*
~ *Educational*
   interests (such as
   evening classes/
   correspondence
   courses)
~ *Watching TV/*
   films
~ *Doing crosswords*
~ *Entering quizzes*
~ *Photography*
~ *PTA activities*

smooth running of the house. You prepare healthy, balanced meals for your family. You remember birthdays and special occasions. You attend school functions and design and put together fancy dress costumes and other clothes. You look after the garden, possibly even growing your own vegetables.

Think about it - you are a highly skilled manager! Look at the other lists. The entries on each one can show you what kind of person you are. If you follow the signs correctly, you can choose the right sort of job according to your personality.

Complete this questionnaire to find out what sort of work would suit you best:

1. **A**. I like routine   YES/NO
   B. I like to be flexible   YES/NO

2. **A**. I prefer to be on my own   YES/NO
   B. I like other people's company YES/NO

3. **A**. I like working with my hands YES/NO
   B. I like paperwork   YES/NO

4. **A**. I am organised and methodical YES/NO
   B. I am disorganised and forgetful YES/NO

5. **A**. I prefer to lead   YES/NO
   B. I prefer to be directed   YES/NO

RESULTS

1. If you like a routine or structure to your day, it is advisable to find a job in which the hours are regular and reliable, and which has a set daily pattern. Larger organisations would probably be your best option

Now make a list of everything you did at school and the qualifications you left with:-

SCHOOL ACTIVITIES

~ Sport (member of athletics team)
~ Prefect/monitor duties
~ Prizes received - essay writing/ reading/languages
~ Writing for school newspaper
Organising activities

QUALIFICATIONS

O levels:
English
Maths
French
Latin
Domestic science
Biology

Practical skills:

Typing/Shorthand/ computer operating (for those who left school more recently)/ demonstrating skills/public speaking.

where a working pattern is already set. For instance, hospitals, large industrial firms, libraries, schools, local government. If you prefer more variation at work, then you need to look elsewhere for something which fulfils this need. It is more likely to be found, for instance, in a small company than in a large organisation. In small companies every member of staff is as vital as the next and usually you will be expected to step in to a number of roles when necessary.

It may be that you think you have a good mixture of both these qualities - in which case you are onto a winning formula. There is a routine part to nearly every job around, so if you can cope with that and be adaptable to change, you will be a prized employee!

2. If you prefer solitary activity, then you should not choose the kind of work which involves mixing with a lot of people. There are many things you can do to match your preferences - research and computer programming, for instance, and some driving jobs. If on the other hand you love being with people, then you can choose from shop work, being a company representative, hotel management, personnel management, teaching, social work, nursing - the list is endless.

Again, it may be that you like a bit of both. If you don't always want to be surrounded by others, don't choose something in which you have no choice. The ideal for you would be something in which you have the opportunity to get out and meet others, but also the space in which to work alone.

3. If you like working with your hands, you will prefer something practical. Cooking; gardening; decorating; dress-making; designing posters/cards and nursing are some of the jobs which may suit you. Alternatively, something with less of a practical emphasis will suit if you prefer less physical activity. Sedentary work such as accountancy, management or secretarial may be more the ticket!

4. If you are particularly proud of your organisational abilities and are able to plan ahead then you should aim for work in the following areas; local government, accountancy, banking, management, marketing, secretarial work. Not all of us can be fantastic organisers - if you're not, see where else your strengths like and go for something which doesn't have inflexible routines and deadlines such as retailing, demonstrating products, or reception work amongst others.

5. If you thrive on making decisions and influencing others, find a job in which your leadership qualities will be fully exploited. If you want to take charge, organise, and negotiate, you would be most fulfilled in either a managerial position or even by starting your own business. Teaching is another field in which you could thrive.

If, however, you prefer to leave the decision making to someone else, you would be better as part of a team. Something like the fire service, for instance, or the police force which would provide you with the opportunity of playing an invaluable supporting role.

PREPARING YOUR CURRICULUM VITAE

Don't panic because you feel that you've nothing to put in it! A C.V. is useful to employers because it gives them chance to see at a glance what sort of person you are. Remember that if you've been bringing up the kids for the last 15 years, most employers will realise that this means you are probably stable, reliable and full of common sense. And don't just include educational and job details - include details of hobbies or activities which show that you're full of the qualities required for the job. If, for instance, you're applying for a job which requires organisational skills and you've spent years organising slimming clubs, or helped with your children's school activities, then put it in the C.V. Anything, in fact, which shows you to have motivation and initiative is useful.

You will notice that educational and career details are given in reversed chronological order - there is a growing preference amongst many employers for this style of C.V. Employers are much more interested in what you've been doing recently than in what you were doing 20 years ago! The more traditional chronological lay out, is still an acceptable option, so feel free to use that style if you wish.

WHAT NEXT?

OK - so you know which kind of work would suit you best. You also know now whether you need to retrain in order to achieve your goal and your C.V. is ready. Over the page is an example of what a good C.V. should look like:

CURRICULUM VITAE

Name: Susan Parker

Address: 25 Turner Terrace
                     Whinney Nook

Daytime Tel: 000-0000

Date of Birth: 2.3.48

EDUCATION:

1988-1989   Secretarial College   Refresher course:
                                            Typing/shorthand

1964-1965   Secretarial College   Typing 50 wpm
                                            Shorthand 100 wpm

1959-1964   Whinney Nook High School O Levels Maths
                                            English
                                            French
                                            Biology
                                            Physics

CAREER

1970-88   Bringing up family

1968-70   Acme Trading Company: Personal Assistant to
                     Managing Director

1965-68   Whinney Nook Council: Shorthand Typist

HOBBIES AND INTERESTS

Reading; writing short stories; involvement in local
PTA; organising events at local community centre
for disabled people.

You will probably still be experiencing some feelings of self-doubt. Well, don't! Thinking positively is the key to your success. Do you really think all those efficient looking people with briefcases you've seen walking around have never felt twinges (or worse) of nervousness and even fear? Of course they have - but the reason they have achieved their goals is that *they* took control of their feelings. They made a decision to be positive about their goals. So if you still need another boost of self-confidence before you get around to actually sending off your application, try looking back at your list of skills and achievements and recognise them as such. If you can run a house, you can certainly do a job efficiently.

NOTE:

Only think about what you can achieve.

You have a lot to offer to an employer. You have to persuade them of this. If you have faith in yourself, so will others.

FINDING THE RIGHT JOB

If you don't find anything you fancy in your local press or jobcentre, why not try targeting a few firms yourself? Find out about local businesses, shops and factories and contact them direct. This is how I got my very first job when I left school - I struck lucky and the firm I had written to happened to have a vacancy coming up a month later. One of the main benefits of this method of job-hunting is that the firm or shop in question is likely to They will perceive you as someone who takes control and who shows initiative. Be warned though - there is obviously a higher risk of rejection with this method of job-hunting. If they haven't advertised a vacancy, it is likely that there isn't one. But you may write to the right place at the right time and your job application may

REMEMBER

*With the direct
approach you
need to target
as many places
as possible*

coincide with their needs. Also some companies are very good at keeping people's applications on file for future consideration - if you've made an impact of any kind, they may remember you the next time they need someone.

It is better to write than to telephone initially. Once you've written to the company, give them two weeks in which to respond. If you still hear nothing, then give them a ring. It's perfectly reasonable to expect a response to an enquiry of this kind. Your initial letter should be brief and to the point. Find out if the company has a personnel department - if so, address the letter to them. If not, find out who the overall manager is and write to him or her. For example:

Dear Mr Davis

I am writing to find out about possible job vacancies within your company/shop/factory, and I enclose my Curriculum Vitae.

I have recently completed a refresher course in secretarial/computing/sales/public relation skills and I am keen to work in banking/the media/cosmetics/fashion.

I would appreciate the opportunity of meeting you and telling you more about myself, and I am available for interview during working hours. I look forward to hearing from you.

Yours sincerely

If you are applying for an advertised position, the letter should look something like this:-

Dear Ms Jones

With reference to the advertisement in tonight's edition of the Evening News, I am applying for the post of Secretary/Sales Assistant/Bank Clerk, and I enclose my Curriculum Vitae as requested.

As you will see from my C.V. I have recently completed a course in word processing skills and am now eager to put these skills into practice.

I am available for interview during working hours and I look forward to hearing from you.

Yours sincerely

As you can see, the letters are brief and to the point whilst drawing attention to details which may work in your favour such as a recently acquired skill. It is vital that you read the advertisement very carefully and supply only what you have been asked for.

THE INTERVIEW!

For many people, the interview itself can be the most stressful part of finding a job. But there are ways in which you can make it less frightening.

1. MAKE SURE YOU PREPARE FOR THE INTERVIEW

We all know that if we feel sure about a subject or a situation we are less likely to feel stressed or anxious about it. If you can prepare well enough to feel that you could answer any question in an interview, you will feel less worried. The worst scenario is for you to be sitting outside the interview room waiting to go in and thinking 'I hope they don't ask me this or that'. The odds are they *will* ask you the question you've been dreading. But if you do your research and planning for the interview carefully, you can feel more confident.

Follow these tips and you can't go far wrong:

- **Find out more about the company. There may be brochures describing what they sell or the services they provide - read them; watch out for company advertisements in the local press. Knowledge of the company and its aims will impress interviewers, and showing that you've done some research will prove to them that you have initiative.**
- **Decide which of your personal qualities will be valuable to the company if you get the job. Think about what you can use as your selling point during the interview. For instance, if you know the job entails meeting members of the public much of the time, stress your ability to communicate well with people and think of a situation which could illustrate this ability.**
- **Look back at your lists of personal qualities, skills and interests. Now write a new list of things you think would make you a valuable asset to the potential employer. If you've done your research properly, you should know what image the company likes to project and what your job would entail if your application is successful. Don't be bashful here - remember, you are selling yourself to the employer. If you don't recognise your qualities, no one else will either!**
- **Now ask a friend or a member of your family to enact a mock interview with you. Here are some questions you are likely to be asked in any interview:**

INT So tell me, Mrs Smith, why are you interested in working for this company?

YOU I like the products you sell, and I like the idea of working within a large organisation/small company.

INT And what makes you think you would be suitable for the position of personal assistant?

YOU Well, I'm reliable, discreet and loyal. I have a proven record of organisational ability and I believe those are the qualities required for this position. I've also recently completed a refresher course in typing and shorthand, and have acquired word processing skills.

INT I can see from your C.V. that you haven't had a job for some time - tell me why.

YOU I've been working at home for the last 15 years bringing up my children and running our busy household.

INT And why do you want to start working now?

YOU My children have grown up now and I feel that my job is done at home. Organising such a busy household was very stimulating when the children were younger, and I'd like to put my skills and talents to use outside the home now that I have the opportunity.

INT You say you have taken some refresher courses - did you enjoy going back to college?

YOU I loved it - I found that I enjoyed learning so much more than I did when I was younger. I think the more mature you are, the better able you are to apply yourself to tasks and situations which would have at one time seemed daunting.

INT What do you think the duties of a personal assistant are?

YOU Well, as personal assistant to the M.D., I would be his organisational base. I would keep his diary, liaise with clients, keep his paperwork up to date and keep a check on on-going projects. In short, I would shield him from unnecessary problems and provide him with a smoothly-run office.

INT Thank you - I think that's all we need to know for now. Do you have any questions to ask us?

YOU I'd like to know about the practical aspects of the job. For instance, what hours I'll be expected to work.

OR Could you tell me about the salary?

OR When will I hear the results of my application?

POINTS TO REMEMBER ABOUT THE INTERVIEW
Wear appropriate clothes - you should aim to look smart and clean but above all wear something you feel relaxed in. It's not advisable to rush out and buy something new for an interview. Choose a reliable outfit from your existing wardrobe which you know suits you and which you feel comfortable in. If you feel good, you will look good too.

Be punctual - if you can arrive ten minutes early so that you can go to freshen up. Be friendly and polite to the receptionist or whoever is showing you into the interview - they may be asked their opinion of you later!

When you're waiting to go into the interview, don't smoke and don't accept any coffee. If the interviewer comes out and you're in the middle of a ciggie and a drink, they will only get in the way and won't create a very good impression.

Don't smoke in the interview, even if you're offered a cigarette and even if the interviewer is smoking. It is best to keep your hands free and to avoid tying yourself in physical knots. Begin the interview sitting comfortably straight in your chair and keep your legs uncrossed, with your feet a few inches apart. Rest your hands in your lap in a relaxed fashion. This will not only help you to feel cool and relaxed, but will also provide some useful body language for the interviewer. You will appear open and confident, with nothing to hide.

Remember that the interviewer is probably seeing candidates every 30 minutes throughout the day. What he or she wants is for both of you to enjoy the interview as much as possible.

When you are shown into the interview room, take three or four discreet deep breaths - this will help to relax you. Sit down and look the interviewer in the eye - if you frequently avoid their eyes you may come across as lacking in confidence.

During the interview, listen carefully to each question and take any time needed to think about your answer. Don't interrupt the interviewer when he or she is talking. If you don't understand the question, ask for an explanation. Doing this displays a certain confidence to the interviewer. Don't talk too much - this will only make you feel nervous and the interviewer feel bombarded. Do elaborate, however - monosyllabic answers don't help either. So give full and relevant answers to the questions and, if you feel that you can add something about yourself which *is* relevant to that particular point, by all means mention it.

WHAT IF I DON'T GET THE JOB?

Positive thinking can help you to cope with rejection. Remember the chapter on dealing with problems through positive thinking? Well here's an opportunity to put all that theory into practice.

- see each interview as a positive experience and learn from them. The more practice you get at interviews, the better you'll be at them.
- the decision not to appoint you doesn't mean you are awful or inadequate. It may have been taken for any number of reasons - they may be promoting from within the company; they may have had 500 applicants or they may genuinely feel that you wouldn't be happy in that position.
- everybody has had to cope with rejection at some point in their lives. Ask any writer, for instance, and they will be able to show you drawers full of rejection letters from publishers. So don't give up. You must use your experiences to improve your performance next time.

CHAPTER NINE

RETIREMENT~A REASSESSMENT

CHAPTER NINE

RETIREMENT ~
A REASSESSMENT

WHAT DOES RETIREMENT MEAN TO YOU?

It can mean a wonderful period of your life when you fulfil your ambitions, spend more time with your partner, feel free of obligation, and generally relax after your years of hard work. To many people, though, retirement does not fulfil expectations. In some cases people have probably not planned for their retirement, either practically or psychologically. With any major lifestyle change like retirement, planning is essential. Problems you suffered before retirement won't magically disappear. Any stress-related problems may be exacerbated by fresh problems when you retire unless you learn to deal with them separately.

MAKE A LIST OF ALL THE AREAS IN YOUR LIFE, FOR EXAMPLE:

~ Being at home - the adjustments
~ Health
~ Finance
~ Fitness

It may be that you are already retired, or perhaps coming up to retirement; whichever it is you have the power within you to take control of your life and to make retirement a happy and fulfilling experience. Don't see retirement in negative terms. It can be a happy and positive time if you plan for it carefully and are aware of some of the potential problems. Now let's look at each of these areas in turn.

ADJUSTING TO BEING TOGETHER

Apart from holidays and weekends, many people have spent little time together even though they live in the same house . Suddenly finding that you are together 7 days a week, 52 weeks a year can come as a bit of a shock if you haven't fully considered the practical arrangements.

RETIREMENT – A REASSESSMENT

EXAMPLE : Take Annie and Bill. They have been married for 30 years and are both fit and healthy, they know they will have enough money to enjoy their retirement, the mortgage has been paid off on the house and the children have left home and are settled elsewhere. Sounds idyllic, doesn't it?

Bill retires at 60, having had a fulfilling and successful career as a manager with a large company. Although they have talked about financial matters in the period leading up to Bill's retirement, neither of them has ever really sat down and thought about what his retirement would actually mean to their lives. And more importantly, they haven't discussed how they will both feel after Bill has retired.

For the first couple of weeks Bill cheerfully gets on with all those jobs around the house that he never had time to do when he was working. Annie is delighted. Meanwhile she carries on with her life, doing the housework, visiting friends and going on the regular outings she has always enjoyed. Then one day, when Annie is out, Bill decides to rearrange the kitchen cupboards. It makes much more sense to have the crockery here and food over there, Bill thinks. Annie is furious when she arrives home, but Bill cannot understand why Annie is so angry. They have a huge row and from then on, it never stops. Not only does Bill constantly 'interfere', as Annie sees it, but he seems to be taking over her life. She feels 'invaded' by his presence when he follows her wherever she goes around the house. Feelings of frustration and resentment grow on both sides and the rows are frequent.

Suddenly, that idyllic picture of retirement has vanished. Both of them are manifesting signs of depression and anxiety. But why has this happened? Because they have not sat down together at any point and discussed their feelings. As a result, both are feeling bewildered as to why their comfortable and enjoyable lives have been so disrupted. Having Bill at home has become a burden rather than a pleasure. Bill, on the other hand, cannot understand why Annie has become so snappy with him, Why doesn't she want him to help around the house? He also feels isolated because while he never had time for any hobbies or pastimes when he was working. Annie has a full and varied social life. Now Bill feels bored and excluded when Annie goes out to carry on her social life.

SOLUTIONS If this scenario is familiar to you, don't panic - things can be put right with a bit of work and lots of understanding. And if you are coming up for retirement, you are in the best position to prepare so that this situation doesn't happen in your house.

1.DISCUSS YOUR FEELINGS

It is vital that you talk things through and find out how you are both feeling. Remember that with one or both of you working full-time for many years, you will not know each other as well as you may think you do. You have, after all, spent more time apart than together. Don't discuss your feelings when you're angry or upset. Wait until the anger has passed, assess the situation and tell your partner how you feel, calmly and with sympathy. If you feel your privacy has been invaded, remember that your partner probably won't understand why you're angry. Explain that the house is your career. It would be as if you had come into his office to suggest and implement all sorts of changes behind his back. Above all, listen to the other person properly. Give the situation proper thought and consideration and together you should be able to come up with a workable solution to your differences.

2.COMPROMISE IS THE NAME OF THIS GAME

You can only come to a satisfactory arrangement through compromise. If one person gives in and feels as though they're making some sort of sacrifice, it won't be long before bitter resentment sets in. But if you both know that each of you is making an effort to help the other, you will respect those efforts. So, in Annie and Bill's case, it may mean that Annie will have to hand over some responsibilities to Bill. And Bill could find some interests and hobbies of his own so that Annie is free to carry on her social life as normal, without being questioned about where she is going.

3.PRIVACY AND TOGETHERNESS

No, this is not a contradiction in terms - it is possible to retain your privacy while achieving a comfortable level of togetherness. Doing absolutely everything together is not the ideal situation. You may feel stifled, vulnerable and too dependent on the other person. Doing everything separately is not the answer either. Having no joint interests or activities may alienate you from each other.

The ideal situation is one in which you both develop some interests and activities which are separate and individual, while also making sure you do some things together. Joining a class together, going on an outing once a week, or seeing a film together - it could be anything at all. This way you will both have things in you life which are interesting to the other person as well as interests which are mutually enjoyable.

4. SPLIT THE CHORES

Make a list of the household chores. Decide between you who prefers to do which chores and do your jobs at the same time. You both have to give a bit here - does it really matter if the other person doesn't dust in the same way you always have? Relax your standards a little and life will be a lot more pleasant.

5. LAUGH A LOT

FACT

laughing is good for you.

Part of the process of rediscovering the pleasures of being together is learning to laugh at yourselves and at each other. Instead of letting a trivial annoyance get out of hand, try and learn to laugh at silly mistakes or habits. After all, being retired should mean having a good time!

The example used presupposes a traditional relationship of marriage where the woman has stayed at home and the man has worked full-time. With each new generation come changes which challenge this traditional status quo. Increasingly both partners work full-time and therefore will retire together. The same rules apply to those people. Sit down, discuss your feelings and work things out together.

But what if you are not married, or if you are widowed?

RETIREMENT AND THE SINGLE PERSON

People who live on their own, for whatever reason, will need to work at finding happiness in retirement just as couples do. They will probably feel a sense of loss in their lives. Work, after all, provides us with a large social outlet and for some people it can sometimes be the only time they are not alone. Again, there are many ways in which you can avoid being lonely. People can be lonely because they may feel that they have nothing to offer the outside world. Without the excuse of a job in common, many people fear that they cannot make friends or be interesting to others. This is not true. You must have faith in yourself and your qualities for others to like you. Make a list of what you think your qualities are. Pick out your strongest quality and repeat it to yourself throughout the day, when you wake up, in the middle of the day, and before you go to sleep. Say, for instance, 'I am an interesting person.' The more you tell yourself this, the more you will believe it and your self-esteem will grow. (See Chapter on **Positive Thinking** for further details of how this exercise works).

I'M LONELY - WHAT CAN I DO?

Monday
am : do washing
pm: visit friends

Tuesday
am: clean bedrooms
pm: see film

Wednesday
am: clean kitchen
pm: pottery class/
    voluntary work

Thursday
am: do gardening
pm: have friends
    over for tea

Friday
am: do shopping
pm: relax in front
    of TV

Above all, remember that you can be in control of your life. Only you can decide not to be lonely. It will take effort but it will be worth it!

Create a routine for yourself. Keep a weekly diary and write everything down that you do and plan to do . Spread your household chores out so that you do some each day. Perhaps you prefer to get the chores out of the way in the mornings, in which case you can keep your socialising for the afternoons and evenings.

If you organise your days and plan what to do, you will really begin to value and get the most out of your available time. You must, of course, keep the routine flexible. On some days, for instance, you might not feel like doing the chores or seeing your friends or going to your pottery class. You must give yourself time for relaxing; after all, isn't retirement all about doing what you want to do at last?

'THAT'S ALL VERY WELL BUT I'VE GOT NO FRIENDS'
There are many different ways of making friends. Why
not try some of these tips and see how you can achieve
a genuinely fulfilling lifestyle:

1.**Learn something new**. Keep your mind agile by
   joining a class in something you already like or have
   always wanted to have a go at. Think about the end of
   term parties, drinks after the class and meeting all
   those like-minded people.

2.**Work in the community**. Voluntary workers are
   welcomed everywhere. Perhaps you could teach your
   newly acquired skills to someone else. You could, for
   instance, start organising trips out for local people in
   the same position as you, advertising in newsagents'
   windows

3.**What about education?** Did you know that
   approximately one in ten of all Open University
   students are over the age of 60? Just think what your
   breadth and depth of knowledge of life could bring to
   a degree course and what wonderful new friends you
   could make.

4.**Is there someone in your street or road who is
   a retired single person?** If so, invite them out to tea
   one day, or to the art gallery with you. They are
   probably feeling as lonely as you are and would feel so
   flattered at being asked.

Remember: it is up to you. If you decide to have fun, you
will succeed. And if you seem as though you're having
fun and leading and interesting life, you will have as many
friends as you like.

BEREAVEMENT

When we were recording the *Lifeguide* series we talked to several women who had lost their partners. Many of them described it as utterly devastating and some said they had felt as though they had been physically damaged by the shock and the grief. Their collective message was optimistic - you do recover from bereavement and you are able to enjoy your life again. This is not to say, however, that you forget the person who has died, but you can learn to come to terms with the loss.

NECESSARY GRIEF

Grieving for someone who has died is normal and it can take many different forms. People who have lived through the experience of bereavement have described feeling many different kinds of emotion during their period of grieving. The shock of someone close to you dying often leaves you feeling numb; one woman we met said that the first six weeks after her husband died were hard to remember.

You may feel angry when someone dies, and this anger may be directed at the people around you or even at the person who has died. This anger is often accompanied by strong feelings of guilt. You may feel guilty because you feel you didn't do enough for the person when he or she was alive, or perhaps you feel guilty about your feelings of anger or even relief. These feelings can often occur if the person who has died was ill for a long time before dying. If you have been caring for that person, relief at their death is an understandable reaction.

Denying the death is another common response to someone close dying. For a while you may see people around who resemble the person you have lost and you will momentarily believe that the person is not dead at all. Once you start to accept that the person is dead, then you can be sure that you are going to feel better. You must let the person go in your mind. Once you have done this, you will start to feel interested in life again.

WHAT CAN I DO TO HELP MYSELF?

1. It is advisable to be involved in the practical things to be done when someone has died. Dealing with death certificates and funeral arrangements can be useful in helping you to come to terms with the death and in helping you to grieve.

2. See your doctor and get help with any physical upsets; you may find that you are having difficulty sleeping and eating. Accept some sleeping pills for a limited amount of time. The pills should be used not to avoid your grief, but to enable you to get some sleep in the first few difficult days. Your appetite will probably return naturally within a week or two and in the meantime drink plenty of milk.

3. Avoid making any major decisions about your life in these early days of grief. Give yourself six months before you decide for instance to either sell your house or stay in it or to live with your children or other relatives.

4. Avoid the temptation to become a social recluse. Accept the invitations to go out. It is advisable to begin new interests and hobbies and meet new friends. After all, you are beginning a new life on your own.

5. Above all, don't deny your grief. If you suppress your feelings, it may lead to depression later on. The feelings won't go away; you must learn to accept them

and cope with them. Grief is a process through which you can live - don't be afraid to ask others for help and support. Just remember that you will feel better in time, but only if you have had your period of grief.

HEALTH AND FITNESS

With a healthy balanced diet and plenty of fresh air and exercise, you will be able to enjoy an active retirement. Have regular check-ups with your doctor and ask his or her advice on any exercise you are considering taking up.

SLEEP

When you were working, your sleep pattern was dictated by the clock. You had to be awake and up at a certain time every day and sleeping later at weekends was a luxury. But in retirement you have the advantage of being able to sleep and wake at your leisure. Attractive as this may sound, many people find the change in their sleep patterns disturbing. So what can you do if you are forever having 'bad nights'?

- **examine your routine. Forget any notions of bedtime. It may have been a certain time when you were working because you wanted to ensure that you had enough sleep before getting up at 6.30 am. Now you can afford to go to bed later, and possibly stay in bed later in the morning. So when it gets to 10.30 pm and you usually go to bed at this time, ask yourself if you are really tired. If not, stay up another hour or two.**

- **allow yourself to nap during the day. You will probably wake after an hour or so feeling refreshed and ready for some afternoon activity. The more active you are during the day, the more easily you will sleep at nights.**

If your inability to sleep becomes a more serious problem which you think is affecting your health and sense of well-being, then you must seek help from your doctor. It may be that your lack of sleep is caused by depression or by a medical problem.

DIET

NOTE:

Never cut down on food bills - *you can economise elsewhere, but food is vital*

Regular eating is an important factor in staying healthy during retirement. Make sure you have at least one balanced meal each day. Now that you have the time, make breakfast a regular pleasure and make leisurely plans about the day ahead.

Try having your main meal at lunchtime instead of in the evenings; you are more likely to use up the food with activity in the afternoon and therefore avoid it being stored as excess fat. Similarly, if you avoid eating main meals soon before you go to bed, you can avoid problems with your digestion. Certain nutrients are more vital to you when you get older; you need protein, calcium and some carbohydrate. You also need a good balance of the right sort of fats and vitamins and minerals in your diet too. For more details about nutrition turn to the *diet* section in Chapter Two

Don't worry if you put on a little extra weight when are older - it will be impossible to recreate the figure you had when you were in your 20s so don't try. Avoid crash diets. You can avoid becoming obese by choosing to eat sensibly and adopting a realistic exercise routine. If in any doubt at all, consult your doctor. He or she will be able to advise you about what to eat and what exercise is right for you.

RETIREMENT – A REASSESSMENT

FITNESS

Before you start doing any exercise, consult your GP.
Being fit complements your healthy diet; fitness and
correct nutrition combine to give you extra energy, a
more supple body and greater strength. But be gentle
with yourself; you're not aiming for the next Olympics
after all. You simply want to achieve a healthy level of
fitness. Here are a few types of gentle exercise which you
can adapt to suit your own pace:

Walking ~ You may not feel that you are exercising
when you are walking but it is in fact a very valuable form
of getting fit and keeping fit. Try walking to the next bus
stop instead of using the one right outside your house.
Alternate the pace, in between lamp posts for instance.
Walk briskly from one to the other, then use a slower
pace to the next lamp post. Repeat this pattern
throughout your walk. Breathe deeply and regularly. If
you do this frequently, you will find in time that you can
walk further and further every day.

Swimming ~ This is a wonderful form of exercise and is
particularly beneficial for anyone suffering from physically
inhibiting medical conditions such as arthritis. Movement
in water is easier because you become, in effect,
weightless.

Dancing ~ This is a wonderful option as it is not only a
great form of exercise, but a terrific way of meeting
people. Check what is available in your area; if there is
nothing that suits you why not consider organising the
dancing yourself? All you need is the local church hall, a
record player or a piano, and a few like-minded people!?

FINANCE

Even though you have no salary coming in to the house now that you have finished working, there are many financial advantages to being retired.

WORKING IS EXPENSIVE!

Just think of the money you have spent over the years on, for instance, clothes for work. And the lunches and snack breaks - unless your company provided a subsidised cafeteria, you probably relied heavily on expensive convenience foods. Travel is probably the greatest saving you'll make - unless you lived within walking distance of your job, most people spend a minimum of £5 a week on travelling alone.

COPING WITH YOUR NEW FINANCIAL SITUATION

There are ways in which you can make savings without lowering your standard of living.

1. YOUR HOUSE

Consider moving to a smaller place - smaller doesn't mean less comfortable or luxurious; you will find that the running costs are lower, and it is easier to maintain. There a may be a committee which takes care of the gardening and upkeep of the building on your behalf.

If you are in rented accommodation, your local housing authority will be able to give you fuller details of the National Mobility Scheme, set up to help tenants to move to different areas of the country when those tenants have special needs. You can get booklets published by the Department of the Environment from your local Citizens Advice Bureau or from the local council. You will find information about accommodation and benefits available to you.

2. STAYING PUT

If you do decide to stay in your present house, however, there are ways in which you can cut down the costs.

Is your house well insulated? Double glazing and loft or cavity insulation will save you a fortune in your heating bills. Ask your local council for details of grants available to help with the costs of insulating your house. A leaflet entitled '*Save money on loft insulation*' is available too.

Consider taking in a lodger - but get advice first from the Citizens Advice Bureau. This does need very careful consideration and planning.

If you are over 70 years old, you may get financial help from the **Mortgage Annuity Scheme** where a mortgage is arranged on your house or flat. The money is used to buy an annuity for you and taxable income will be paid to you from that annuity for the rest of your life. This means that the house is still yours and you are free to leave it to whoever you wish in your will. The beneficiary will have to sell the house in order to pay off the loan, but the rest of the capital gained by selling would then be theirs.

If you are eligible for the **Home Reversion Scheme**, it means that your house will be sold but you will retain the right to live there for the rest of your life with either income payments on a regular basis or a lump sum. You will have to pay rent and you will be responsible for maintaining the property. This scheme is available from some insurance companies and building societies.

You can get advice on both of these options from your local Citizens Advice Bureau.

3. YOUR CAR

Consider exchanging your car for a smaller, more economical model. Buy one which uses less fuel and therefore gives you more miles per gallon, and a model which it is easy to get the parts for. A smaller car may cut down on insurance costs too. Remember that it's not simply the cost of petrol - maintenance and repairs can be very expensive.

Another option is to sell the car and use public transport. Obviously if you are living in a remote location, then a car is necessary. But decide whether you are near enough to local hospitals, libraries, shops and recreation facilities to give up your car. Perhaps there is an excellent public transport system in your area

4. ORGANISE YOUR BUDGET

Make sure that you know all the facts. Do visit your local council and Citizens Advice Bureau to make sure that you are receiving all the benefits and grants you are eligible for. Then review your income and outgoings. Making a list is advisable.

Allow room within this budget for holidays and emergencies. Being retired doesn't mean that you will appreciate your holidays any less. And it is advisable to have an emergency kitty set aside - this way you don't have to worry about forgotten bills plopping through the letterbox.

And remember, there are some part-time jobs you could do which could help if you do have financial difficulties. Find out what you are allowed to earn before your earnings become taxable - again, the CAB will be able to advise you on this.

RETIREMENT - A POSITIVE PLEASURE

Like any other stage in your life, retirement requires careful planning and preparation. See it as a positive experience when you can enjoy life to the full. Think of all the benefits of retirement - you are free of the worries and anxieties that come from just being young and inexperienced; rediscover the pleasures of being with your partner; fulfil some long-standing ambitions; travel; exploit the fact that your time is now your own.

Don't underestimate the need to adapt positively to your new lifestyle - but if become aware of any potential problems and confront them when they arise, you can truly make the most of your new freedom.

Retiring is not the end, but the beginning of a new and positive stage in your life

A FINAL WORD

THE POWER OF POSITIVE THINKING

This book does not claim to be able to solve all your problems for you. But we do hope that it can give you the inspiration you need to believe that you can be happier and can achieve a better quality of life by adopting a philosophy of positive thinking.

Positive thinking introduces the concept of choice to your life - the choice to be happy, calm, healthy, and successful. It means making changes to your lifestyle and your attitudes and confronting your feelings and responses. Positive thinking is about understanding yourself, making decisions about your life, and learning to help yourself. You can't solve every problem that comes along - sometimes you will need help to sort it out. But positive thinking can prompt you to find that help in the first place.

Above all, positive thinking is not about avoiding problematic events or situations but about liking yourself enough to deal with those problems in a way which is good for you. If you can learn to like yourself, you are well on the way to realising your goals and ambitions.

When we talk of success, we mean success in all areas of your life. Being successful does not necessarily mean being rich and famous. Being successful means achieving your goals - whether it's being slim, being organised, or just being happy. Being successful means learning not to punish yourself when things go wrong or when you make mistakes. Being successful means seeing the potential for happiness and fulfilment in your life. Being successful means looking for the positives rather than dwelling on the negatives, understanding what your needs are and deciding to fulfil those needs.

No one else can do it for you, although when you're dealing with serious problems there are practical resources available which can help you to help yourself. So decide to be a positive thinker and take control of your life - after all, you deserve to be happy, don't you?

INDEX

INDEX

USEFUL INFORMATION

USEFUL INFORMATION : CHAPTER BY CHAPTER

CHAPTER ONE:
POSITIVE THINKING

Bibliography:
Positive Thinking by Vera Peiffer
Strategies of Optimism by Vera Peiffer
Both published by :-
Element Books, Longmead, Shaftesbury,
Dorset

National Council of Psychotherapists and
Hypnotherapy Register, 1 Clovelly Road,
London W5 5HE

National Register of Hypnosis and
Psychotherapy, 12 Cross Street, Nelson,
Lancs BB9 7EN Tel: 0282 699378

CHAPTER TWO :
THE PROBLEM OF WEIGHT

The Mind and Body Diet by Colin Rose
Published by Accelerated Learning Systems
50 Aylesbury Road, Aston Clinton, Bucks
Further information from UNI-VITE
NUTRITION at the same address.

Weight Watchers UK Ltd, 11 Fairacres,
Dedworth Road, Windsor, Berks
0753 856751

Anorexia Aid, The Priory Centre, 11 Priory
Road, High Wycombe, Bucks HP13 6SL

CHAPTER THREE : FEELING FIT

Physical Education Association, c/o North
East London Polytechnic
Lonbridge Road, Dagenham, Essex RMS3 2AS

Body-Check, Department of Movement
Science and Physical Education
The University of Liverpool, PO Box 147,
Liverpool L69 3BX

CHAPTER FOUR : HEALTH

Family Planning Information Service
27-35 Mortimer Street, London W1N 7RJ
Local Family Planning Clinic - in local phone
book

Brook Advisory Clinic - local phone book or
contact the Head Office at:153a East Street,
London SE17 2SD, 071 735 0085

Pre-Menstrual Tension Advisory Service
PO Box 268, Hove, East Sussex BN3 1RW

Breast Care & Mastectomy Association
26a Harrison Street, London WC1H 8JG

Insitute for Complementary Medicine
21 Portland Place, London W1N 3AF

HRT
The Amarant Trust, 14 Lord North Street,
London SW1P 3LD
(Information helpline: 0836 400190)

British Heart Foundation
102 Gloucester Place, London W1H 4DH

Women and Medical Practice - Health
Information Centre (register of alternative
health practitioners)
666 High Road, London N17

CHAPTER FIVE : SMOKING

SMOKERS' QUIT PLAN
ASH - Action on Smoking and Health,
5/11 Mortimer Street, London W1N 7RH

CHAPTER SIX : DEPRESSION

British Association for Counselling
37a Sheep Street, Rugby, Warwickshire
CV21 3EX, 0788 78328/9

Institute of Family therapy
43 New Cavendish Street,
London W1M 7RG, 071 935 1651

National Council of Psychotherapy and
Hypnotherapy
1 Clovelly Road, Ealing, London W5
081 567 0262

British Association of Behavioural
Psychotherapy
Psyychology Department, Dykebar Hospital
Grahamston Road, Paisley, Scotland
041 884 5122

USEFUL INFORMATION

Institute for Transactional Analysis
BM Box 4104, London WC1N 3XX
071 404 5011

The Samaritans - local phone book

Relate - local phone book or head office:
Herbert Gray College, Little Church Street
Rugby, Warwickshire, 0788 73241

Useful publications:
Family Doctor Guides :
Depression by Dr Greg Wilkinson
Published by the British Medical Association

The Counselling Handbook by Susan Quilliam and
Ian Grove-Stephenson. Published by Thorsons
Publishers Ltd, Wellingborough,
Northamptonshire NN8 2RQ

CHAPTER SEVEN : WORK
National Association of Citizens Advice Bureaux
115-123 Pentonville Road London N1 9LZ
071 833 2181
And local phone book

Equal Opportunities Commission
Overseas House, Quay Street
Manchester M3 3HN, 061 833 9244

New Ways to Work
309 Upper Street, London N1 2TY
071 226 4026
(educational charity which promotes job sharing
and flexible working arrangements)

Employment Training information to be found at
local jobcentres

Open University
Central Enquiry Service, PO Box 71
Milton Keynes MK7 6AG

Open college
FREEPOST TK1006, Brentford
Middlesex TW8 8BR, 081 847 7788

Women Returners' Network
The Secretary - Ann Bell, Chelmsford AEC
Patching Hall Lane, Chelmsford Essex
CM1 4DB

Adult Education Centres - run by local education
authority. Contact local council.

Working Mothers' Association
77 Holloway Road
London N7 8JZ

Useful Reading:-
'Grants to Students' - leaflet free from:-
DES Publications Despatch Centre
Honeypot Lane, Canons Park, Stanmore
Middlesex HA7 1AZ

University Degree Courses for Mature Students
- leaflet available from :-
UCCA, PO Box 28 , Cheltenham,
Glos GL50 1HY

Returning to Work A directory of education and
training for women.
Published by Kogan Page Ltd, 120 Pentonville
Road, London N1 9JN.

CHAPTER NINE - RETIREMENT
Pre-Retirement Association
19 Undine Street, London SW17 8PP

Publications:
'Choice' Magazine - available at newsagents or by
subscription from:

Choice
Subscription Department, 12 Bedford Row
London WC1R 4DX